SPACE
TRAVELING

MARK TRAA

For Wendy

© 2005 Rebo International b.v., Lisse, The Netherlands
1st edition 2006 Rebo Publishers

Text and illustrations: Mark Traa
Layout: Minkowsky Graphic Design, Enkhuizen, The Netherlands
Cover layout: Minkowsky Graphic Design, Enkhuizen, The Netherlands
Typesetting: AdAm Studio, Prague, The Czech Republic
Translation: Abandon Agency, Prague, The Czech Republic
Proofreading: Jeffrey Rubinoff, Sarah Dunham

ISBN 90 366 1887 8

SPACE
TRAVELING

MARK TRAA

REBO
PUBLISHERS

Contents

Introduction

Space traveling is a very complex activity. It depends on complicated equipment to carry out intricate processes. This equipment uses state-of-the-art modern technology and that alone should resolve any doubts of their reliability. However, technology is not a complete resolution of our doubts because space travel is carried out by people and it is human nature to make errors.

This book deals mainly with manned space travels and relates the stories of those who risked their lives for space exploration. Hundreds of color photographs give added insight into space mission preparations, daily life on board a space station and the return to Earth. Step by step, you will be shown several aspects of the astronaut´s demanding profession. Attention is given to the tragic accidents in the history of manned space travel as well as to the future of missions to the Moon and Mars.

Space Traveling is mostly a picture book. We do not attempt to offer an exhaustive historiography. The emphasis lies mainly with "modern manned space travel": the era of space shuttles, the Mir space station and the International Space Station (ISS), which covers the last thirty years of human activity in space.

Not many people realize that the press has very little freedom with regards to space missions. Space photographs are only taken by organizations that set up and finance space missions. Many of the events taking place in connection with space missions can be accessed by independent press photographers but they nevertheless need to be registered, and it is therefore very difficult to take a completely unconstrained picture. The subject to be photographed is often so unique that photographers make do within the given restrictions. We will therefore not concern ourselves with the fact that the photos were not made by amateur or independent photographers.

Thousands of photos were sifted through before the final choices for this book could be made. I would like to express my gratitude to all those who have let me browse through their archives or made their pictorial resources available in other ways. I wish to thank Ed Hengeveld, Bert Vis, Sander Koenen, Chris van den Berg, Luc van den Abeelen, ESA/ESTEC (Anneke van der Geest) and Frans Blok. And, above all, I am thankful to Arianne for her invaluable support and help.

Mark Traa

Ready *for space*

Ready *for space*

The immense hall of the Johnson Space Center in Houston houses a number of real size models of the space shuttle and the ISS. Some of the astronauts' practical training takes place in this hangar. The Johnson Center is the home base for American astronauts. Most of them live in the vicinity of the center.

Ask a ten-year-old boy what he wants to be when he grows up and you can be sure to hear that being an astronaut has made the cut. It is hardly surprising: space travelers have a distinctly positive public image similar to that of a racecar driver or a fire fighter. Even for people who have never had ambitions to make it into space, from time to time nearly everyone at least day-dreams about a trip in space. It is fantastic, thrilling, honorable and romantic. And it is still exclusively for a few chosen elite. Up to the present day, no more than five hundred people have traveled outside the Earth's atmosphere.

Still, many astronauts (in Russia they are called cosmonauts) dreamt of missions into space only after such opportunities became realizable. At the end of the fifties, during the Cold War, the Soviet Union and the United States put teams together from among the top jetfighter pilots willing to risk their lives in the forthcoming space race. It was their task to prove that people could survive in space and above all, to make sure that their rival did not achieve too many primacies.

Barring a few exceptions, the first generation of space travelers came from the ranks of the military. The training they received tested them in all the ways doctors and psychologists could think of. After all, nobody knew what they would have to face. Would they be able to live through acceleration, zero-gravity and radiation? In those years, not all scientists were sure they could. For months on end, the astronaut-hopefuls were exposed to extremely difficult tests. They were spun

The crew of 1998 STS-91 flight listens to their instructor during a training in the large hall of the Johnson Space Center in Houston. The hefty astronaut in the background is Valery Ryumin, an experienced Russian cosmonaut who was appointed flight leader but was in fact pushed through to inspect the Mir station.

around in centrifuges, locked in isolation cabins and asked complex psychological questions. Reaction time, stress resistance and ability to improvise had to be proven beyond any doubt. Never had the mind and body been subjected to such an intense battery of tests before. In the United States, these experiments were carried out publicly to a certain extent, whereas in the Soviet Union all preparations were kept under tight control.

American astronauts are based in the NASA-operated Lyndon B. Johnson Space Center in Houston. Most of their training facilities are located there. The Center houses models of the space

shuttle and parts of the International Space Station (ISS) in its immense hangar. There is a simulator of the shuttle cockpit in which pilot and commander can become familiar with the myriads of switches and controls. There is a virtual reality lab which enables astronauts to train in flying as well as spacewalking. There is also a model of a shuttle toilet. Astronauts can practice managing with a 5-inch toilet opening. Beneath the hole there is a camera and a screen on which the astronauts check to see they are in the right position. Nothing is left to chance, not even the most intimate moments of space missions.

Training sessions also take place in other locations in the country. At the launching site in Florida for example, where, besides

Russian cosmonaut Gennady Strekalov slides down an inflatable slide from the opening of a simulator of the space shuttle. Strekalov traveled in March 1995 in a Soyuz capsule to the Mir station and returned in July in a shuttle vehicle. He died in 2004.

Playing around in zero-gravity is surely fun.
Here you can see the crew of a 1992 Shuttle
mission floating in an airplane flying in a special parabola. The plane flies straight up only
to switch off the engines shortly afterwards
and fall. At a safe flight level the plane then
begins a new climb up. At the top of the curve
the passengers for some tenths of seconds
find themselves in zero-gravity.

Page 13:
Astronauts train the launching position of the
space shuttle. In the foreground (with his eyes
shut) is Norman Thagard, next to him his
Russian colleague Vladimir Dezhurov and
Gennady Strekalov. Bonnie Dunbar, an
American, is sitting up straight.

other things, astronauts go through emergency evacuation
drills of shuttle spacecrafts while still grounded. They practice
boarding prepared emergency modules so that in the case of
an emergency, they can slide down the launching towers which
support space shuttle spacecrafts. However, they do not actually try the ride down. It is simply too dangerous. In any case,
such an emergency situation will probably never occur. Once on
the ground they take shelter in a bunker or in an armored vehicle which they can use to escape. Less spectacular, but still
quite substantial, are the practice sessions with experiments
that will be taking place aboard ship.

A great deal of a space traveler's education consists of writing
and listening. Each spacecraft has exceptionally complex
instructions for use. Experts in all possible fields with regard to
the shuttle program lecture astronauts on systems and flight
controls. The theoretical part of an astronaut's training has
since become only more complex after various foreigners
became involved in space missions. Russians learn English,

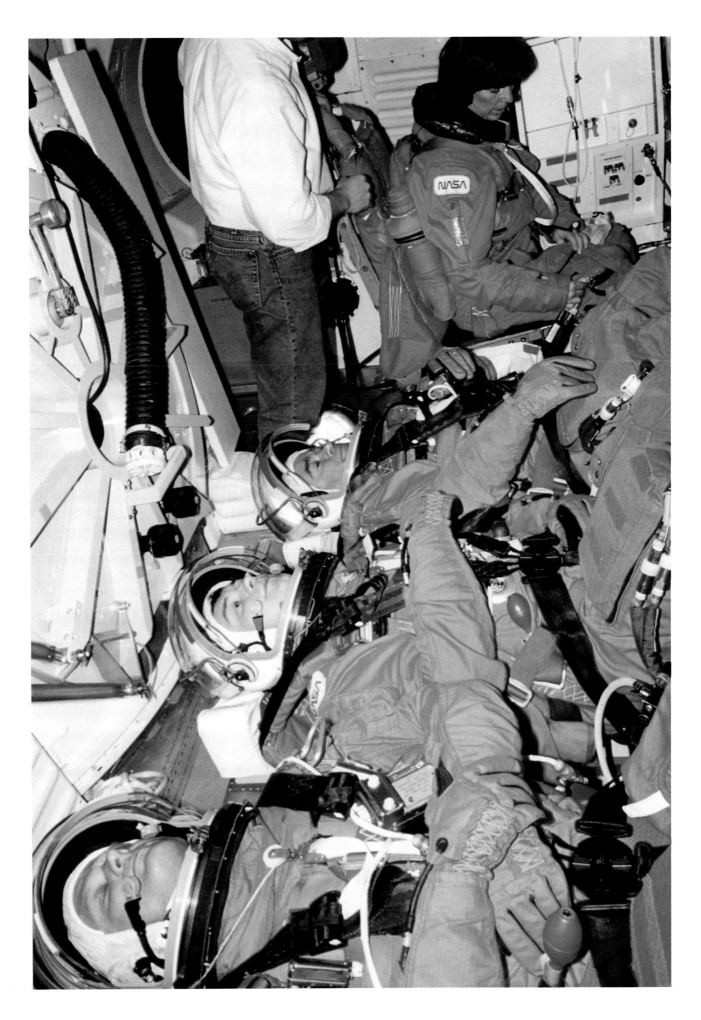

Americans and Europeans acquire at least a basic command of Russian. This is often seen as the most challenging part of the training. The astronauts are subjected to exams on a regular basis: practical ones as well as theoretical ones. In the simulators, astronauts have to adequately solve one emergency situation after another. There are also regular medical check-ups, during which astronauts are sometimes subjected for hours to various tests. These examinations are a definite source of

Who: *Gherman Titov, Russia*
(1935 – 2000)

When: *from 1961*

Why: *Gherman Titov became, shortly after Yuri Gagarin, the world's second man in space at the age of twenty five. He remains the youngest man to have traveled in space. He was in space for twenty-four hours. Titov carried out an excellent mission but after his return he turned out to have a reckless nature. He was involved into a number of implausible car accidents. To the great annoyance of his superiors he was repeatedly stopped by the traffic police in his Volga car. Titov suffered from all the vices of a media star. After he ran away from the Soviet Union he was hailed with great enthusiasm and pomp as a hero in the United States. He received a White House reception and talked to President Kennedy, gave a press conference at the United Nations and visited Ford production plants. He paid no attention to warnings of any sort. Titov would not only drive dangerously, he also had regular quarrels with agents who questioned his behavior. Titov worked as a cosmonaut for ten years and there are grave disciplinary incidents in his files. In 1969, officials got fed up with his behavior. He was not allowed to drive or fly for two years and he got into financial difficulties. Shortly afterwards, Titov left the cosmonaut corps.*

anxiety even for those who feel fit and healthy, because there is always the chance that something wrong will be found and present an obstacle to the trip. Risks are never taken. In many cases, cosmonauts are strongly advised to have their tonsils out as well as to have the weak parts of their teeth repaired prior to a mission.

Back in the fifties, the Soviets set up a whole settlement for their cosmonauts as well as for other personnel: the original name is *Zvezdny Gorodok*, or the Star City in English. In reality, it was a top secret military base, an hour's ride from Moscow. Apartment buildings were erected with stores, restaurants and schools; there were halls with models of spacecrafts, a centrifuge in which astronauts could get used to immense acceleration, and a large swimming pool, which later served for spacewalk practice. The Star City, currently with six thousand inhabitants, was expanded in the sixties and the hall where training models were housed was enlarged. Nowadays, Russian sections of the ISS are kept so that cosmonauts can exercise on the various pieces of highly sophisticated equipment.

The crew of a shuttle mission inspects a cable lift in towers next to a ready-for-launch Space shuttle. In case an emergency situation occurs shortly after the launch, the astronauts can quickly evacuate the ship and can board one of these small units which will then transport them away from the launching pad. These emergency units are located in the upper part of the towers. Once on the ground, astronauts are to take shelter in a tank. Astronauts usually practice only the getting in and out of the unit because this is a rather dangerous drill which will, according to the expectations of most experts, never be needed in reality. Still, this exercise needs to be carried out.

This picture shows evacuation training near the launching pads at the Kennedy Space Center in November 1986. Astronauts take away a wounded technician worker after he was transported from the upper part of launching towers down the so-called cable lift.

Page 17:
Dutch astronaut Wubbo Ockels tests a self-designed sleeping bag prior to his space mission in 1985. Astronauts do not float freely around in this bag as is the case with regular sleeping bags. The invention has not been used since Ockel's flight.

The training part of the base, adjacent to the residential area, looks pretty much like a university campus. There is a statue of the first cosmonaut, Yuri Gagarin, where, faithful to the long tradition, astronauts come to lay flowers before they set out for space. Gagarin also plays a crucial role in the museum which is based in the Star City. In the golden age of Soviet space exploration (in the first half of the sixties) nobody would have thought that Western astronauts would be training in the very same building where Yuri Gagarin went through the preparations for his space flight. In the meantime, an American and a European enclave were set up in the Star City, with its own living quarters and a separate bar.

Since the second half of the nineties, the space programs of the East and West have to a large extent merged together. Naturally, it required some effort from both parties which previously had completely different manners of working. And so the first Americans who visited the Star City were surprised that their Russian colleagues attended meetings equipped merely

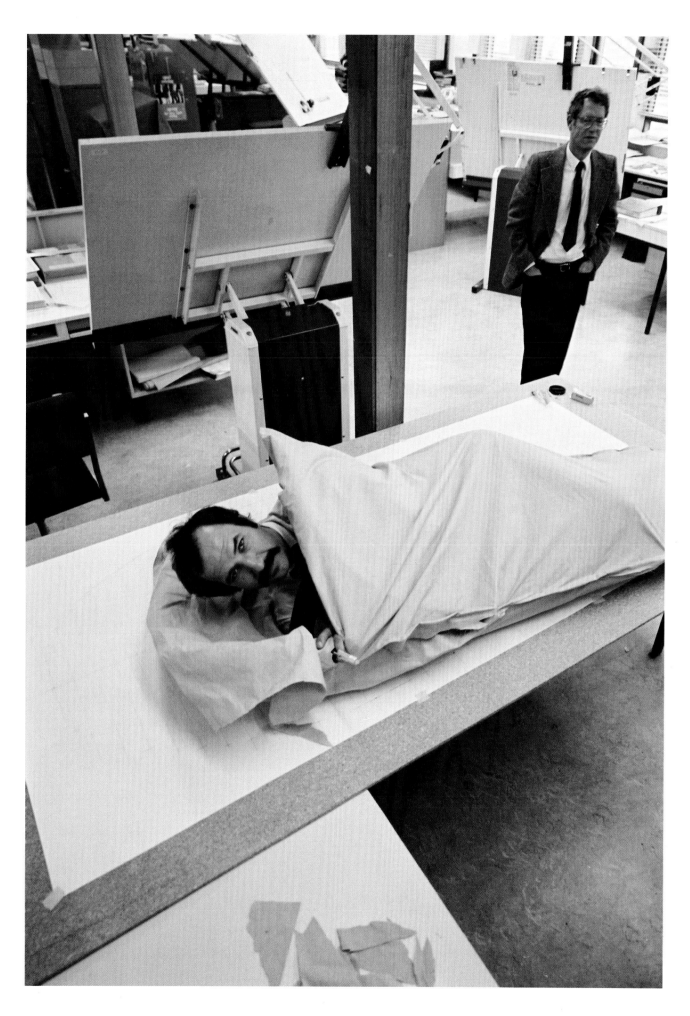

with a pen and piece of paper. In contrast, Americans have a tendency to put every single detail in print. On the Russian side, it turned out that knowledge was sometimes stored only in the heads of certain individuals. To the great surprise of the Americans, some schemas of Russian spacecraft components could not be found—something as simple as a telephone directory or a plan of the Star City did not exist at all.

Blundering astronauts

Astronauts are smart people and that is what they are valued for. They represent their countries in space so surely you do not want any misfits up there. Nonetheless, there have been cases of serious misconduct. Especially in the early years of space exploration, not every married astronaut resisted the temptations of enthusiastic groupies.

In the era of the Soviet empire, when the imperfections of the socialist system were negated and denied, there were cosmonauts who failed on the ground. Now we know that in 1963 three cosmonauts were swept aside with one stroke of a pen; Ivan Anikeyev, Grigori Nelyubov and Valentin Filatyev were caught under the influence in a riot with a military patrol. They were arrested and brought before their commander on duty, who was in fact willing to ignore the incident provided that Filtayev, the initiator of the disturbance, offered his sincere apologies. Filtayev refused and the trio were discharged from active duty. Nelyubov was transferred to an air unit in Siberia where nobody would believe that he had been about to go on a space mission. He died in 1966 when, under the influence of alcohol, he fell under a train near the city of Vladivostok. Filatyev and the others were retouched in a group photo of the first cosmonauts. It was decades before their faces emerged from oblivion and the three regained their place in the history of space exploration.

In America there were astronauts who were suspended because of their disrespect of the rules. The entire crew of the Apollo 15 mission was suspended after the flight when it turned out they had taken envelopes to the moon for commercial purposes. In 1990, shuttle astronaut Robert Gibson was suspended because he had taken part in an air show. According to NASA, he had unnecessarily risked his life. Gibson was taken off the list for the next shuttle mission and was not allowed to fly T-38 jet fighter plane for one year. The same measures were applied to his colleague David Walker who maneuvered too close to a civilian airplane. He could not fly his jet plane for two months and had to abandon his preparations for the next shuttle mission. In 1999, Mark Lee was kicked out of the crew of the ISS due to an alleged conflict with his superiors.

But measures are also taken when an astronaut gets into an unpleasant situation not of his or her doing. Such was the case with Eileen Collins, the first woman commander of a shuttle mission. She was threatened at a presentation by a man who claimed to be crazy about her and promised he would keep on hassling her unless he could meet her. Eventually, that man threatened to kill her at a parade in her native city after a mission. As a result, NASA asked her not to take part in the parade. In 1997, the police arrested a woman who attempted to enter astronaut Story Musgrave's house in Florida. The woman – who committed suicide one year later – had been harassing him for years with phone calls, letters and presents. The well-known television comedian David Letterman was another victim of hers.

It also turned out that Russians disposed of more antiquated technology than the Americans and that not all the equipment had been taken care of as one would have expected in a space center. In the hall which housed the real-sized model of the Soyuz capsule, the windows were covered with faded rags. In

Canadian astronaut Bob Thirsk makes a parachute jump. Later on, in 1996, he had a space flight in the space shuttle.

Eileen Collins.

The STS-84 shuttle mission crew practices an evacuation drill in an armored vehicle close to the launching pads. The crew members got into the tank shortly after they simulated getting down the launch tower in an emergency unit. Once on the ground, the crew can choose between a bunker and a ride in an armored vehicle which will get them away from the highly explosive space shuttle.

a corner, there was a make-shift living room with old armchairs and a profusion of plants. The apparently outdated computers were sealed off with pieces of lace which were fixed on with wax. On the walls, there were yellowed posters of cosmonauts from the past. The floors were covered with thick bundles of cables. In the larger hall, which housed the models of the ISS parts, in the back, there was an enormous heap of rubbish, separated from the rest by a wide curtain, and nobody knew whether someone would ever do something with it. But the foreign guests learned not to laugh at their hosts. They know that the Russians have an exceptionally strong argument for not changing anything about it: it works. All manned Russian spacecrafts are usually launched on time and the last fatal accident happened more than thirty years ago. It is fine as it stands.

But let's return to the selection process for astronauts. Currently, astronauts and cosmonauts do not come exclusively from the ranks of the armed forces. Not everyone who flies to space needs to be an experienced pilot. In the space shuttle, there is space for six astronauts; they are not all required to be familiar with the ins and outs of piloting a spacecraft. A space station does not need to be piloted; as long as it is kept in its pre-programmed trajectory by means of the small propelling rockets, it orbits the Earth without the intervention of the crew. In practice, the commander of a space station often has a military education. Frequently, they were first commanders of a space flight (such as space shuttle missions). Even today, there are many army officers in the service of NASA.

If new astronauts are needed, recruitment advertisements are published. Anyone who thinks that he or she meets the requirements can apply. Except for pilots, most of the recruits have academic backgrounds with careers in research or in commerce. The space agencies can afford to set the standard very high because there will always be enough applicants. Thousands of people usually apply for only a couple dozen vacancies. The majority of them fail in the first round, during which the participants have to fill in rather complex application forms.

The crew of the STS-84 flight is, as part of evacuation training, riding in an M-113 armored vehicle away from the launching pads. Eileen Collins, pilot of the Shuttle Atlantis mission, drives the tank. Later, she will become the first ever female commander of a space shuttle mission.

The selection process becomes more and more attenuated as the number of remaining candidates drops.

It is rather difficult to determine what exactly is critical for selection commissions when choosing and hiring astronauts-to-be. To a large extent, it depends on the particular mission the candidate would take part in: will he or she be able to pilot a space shuttle or live for months on end in an orbital station, carry out experiments as well as maintenance jobs? It is not enough to be an experienced pilot, a scientist or a technician; the person must also be capable of cohabiting with a group, often under difficult circumstances. More than anything else,

an astronaut has to be a team-player and, at the same time, able to solve problems independently. She must be able to see the value of a human presence in space; otherwise missions could be carried out unmanned.

It is also very important that the aspiring astronaut has an exemplary record. After all, he represents his country and will undoubtedly attract immense attention from the media. Especially in the early phases of space travel, astronauts had to have immaculate reputations. Astronauts from both camps were asked to remain silent on the subject of their unstable marriages and especially their extramarital affairs and other improprieties. Their political backgrounds were checked as

In this picture, astronauts of the STS-26 mission, the first mission planned in 1998 after the tragic accident of the Challenger in 1986, board a T-38 fighter jet at the Kennedy Space Center airport. They are there to inspect the progress of work on the Discovery, the space shuttle that was to take them into space.

Page 25:
John Glenn, 77 years of age, gets dressed during a training session for his 1998 space shuttle mission. A NASA employee patiently holds his helmet.

Astronauts Mike Foale and William McArthur together with cosmonaut Valery Tokarev are standing at the edge of a swimming pool in the Johnson Space Center where they are going to practice spacewalking. In the water you can see parts of the ISS. The pool is almost 200 feet long and 33 feet deep. Its capacity is close to 60 million gallons of water.

well; especially in the Soviet Union where some cosmonauts were dismissed for the dissident pasts of their fathers-in-law. Astronauts were expected to be law-abiding citizens, loyal to their wives and with sweet little children. This era is now long gone. However, being a role model to the public remains an important factor.

Those chosen cannot fly immediately. In fact, they are at the start of more challenging training which, under normal circumstances, culminates in their first space mission. A typical astronaut goes through two kinds of training. The first is identical for virtually all candidates. In the United States for instance, every astronaut must go through emergency procedure drills and must understand the functioning of the space shuttle; the same goes for cosmonauts in Russia, but they train for Soyuz spacecrafts. This basic training takes roughly six months. After successful completion, the astronaut does not get on a list for a mission however. Trainees rehearse on devices which are aboard a space ship to carry out experiments, train in spacewalking (a huge water tank is sometimes

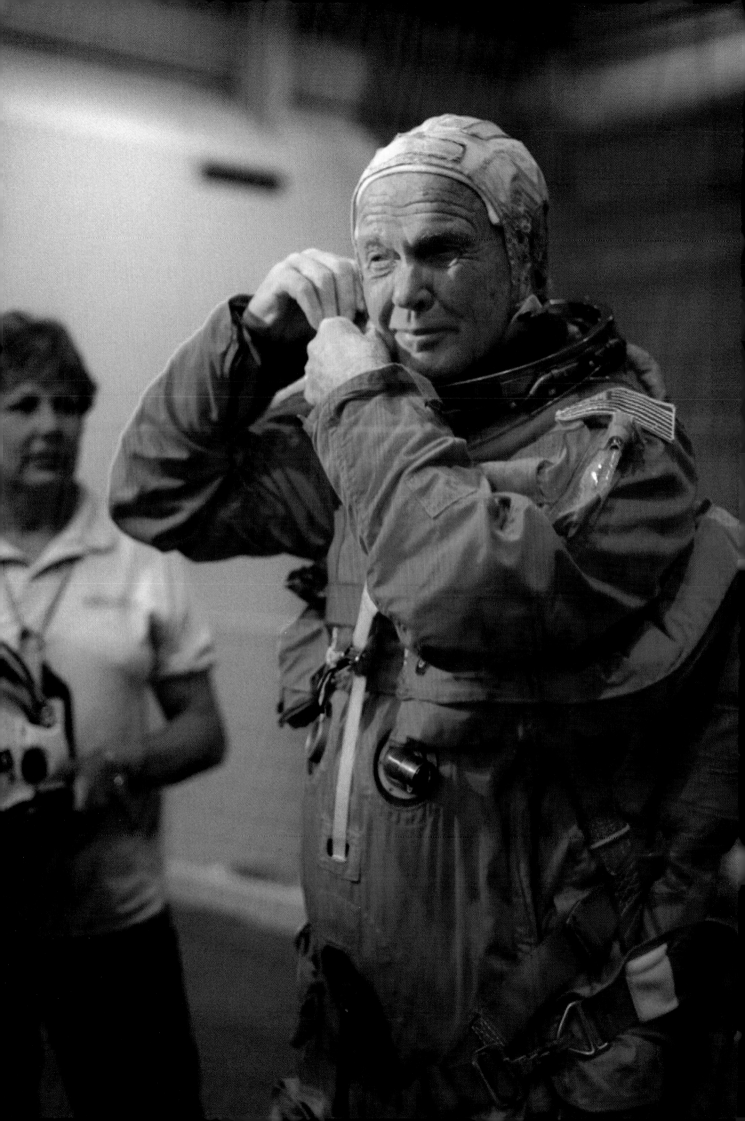

used for this purpose) and last but not least, the trainees become familiar with one another.

The psychological makeup of a crew is crucial, especially if they are to spend a long time together. Particularly in Russia where the emphasis has been on long term missions, the psychologists have a decisive say in who will be sent into space. Several crews have had to be dismissed shortly before their missions due to incompatibility. These are in no way redundant or useless measures; there really have been incidences of things going wrong. Upset or mentally unstable astronauts refused to communicate with other crew members sometimes for days. However, it is usually the flight and mission control crew on

Who: *Gordon Cooper*, USA
(1927 – 2004)

What: *Mercury 9 and Gemini 5*

When: *1963 and 1965*

Cooper is the last American to orbit the Earth alone. Cooper belonged to the first batch of Mercury Seven astronauts. He was also the first astronaut to fly into space twice, in 1965, in the Gemini 5 module. After his flight he took an interest in the study of the paranormal. During his deployment as a pilot in Germany, he claimed to have seen unidentified flying objects. In a book which he published later in his life he presents one conspiracy theory after another. According to Cooper's book, NASA, the US Air Force and the authorities in general have been trying to sweep information of UFO observations under the carpet. Cooper was celebrated by UFO enthusiasts who at last had found a supporter of their theories within the NASA structures and who had in fact been in space.

Earth who are blamed for astronauts' failures; for example, because they are too demanding or require too much from the mission's members. There had been some very tough verbal exchanges between crews and mission controls as a way of venting aggression and frustration. To bridge the divide between the camps, former astronauts now sit in the flight control center and there is always one astronaut nominated as the so-called CapCom (Capsule Communicator, a term from the sixties) who maintains communication with his colleagues in space.

These days, it would be wrong to assume that astronauts must be in superb form or that they have to be super humans like the heroes of the first generation of cosmonauts. Certainly they have to be healthy, but that is something different. There have been people in space since then who certainly would not

An astronaut leaves a space shuttle with a somersault down the emergency slide during evacuation trainings in a pool in Houston.

Canadian astronaut Chris Hadfield is assisted while getting into his space suit and before diving into a training swimming pool.

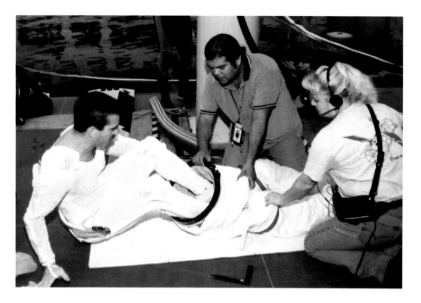

Hadfield has his space suit trousers already on and now, with apparent difficulties, puts on the upper waterproof part of the space suit.

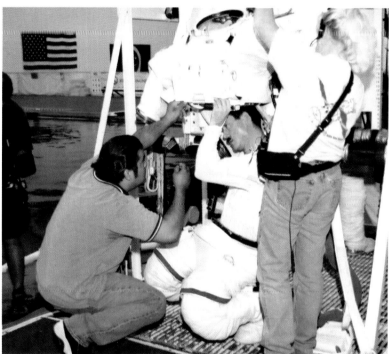

Russian cosmonaut Nikolai Budarin has his space suit helmet put on by his American colleague Donald Pettit. Behind them, there is a swimming pool into which Budarin dives immediately afterwards to practice space-walking.

Page 29:
Space Shuttle pilot Pamela Melroy is helped out of her suit after training. Melroy flew as a jet fighter pilot in a mission during the first Gulf War in 1991 and became a test pilot afterwards. In 1994 she became an astronaut and served twice as a space shuttle mission pilot.

stand up to the standards imposed on the first astronauts. Such is the case with a Japanese TV journalist who paid to be able to fly to the Russian Soyuz station and who turned out to be a chain-smoker and a heavy drinker. And what about John Glenn who orbited the Earth as the first American back in 1962 and returned in the nineties at the age of 77 to make one more trip into space aboard a space shuttle. There have also been American politicians as well as NASA top officials who had already finished their careers as astronauts but still wanted to

Astronauts on the ground

For psychologists, astronauts are subjects of immense interest. They work and live in unusual circumstances and their profession requires a high level of cooperation. Psychologists who focus on group dynamics can truly enjoy themselves when participating on space missions. However, observing human behavior in space is not a simple task. Psychologists and medical doctors therefore concentrate their efforts on ground trainings. In Russia, where the main focus is predominantly on the effects of space missions on the human psyche, this kind of research is quite standard. For some time now, international scientists and test subjects have been invited to join the Russian researchers.

One of these group experiments was called SFINCSS `99, an isolation test which took place in 1999 in Moscow. The experiment took place in a hall inside a replica of the Mir station. Three people from Austria, Canada and Japan were expected to spend 110 days in cylinder-shaped modules where they joined a group of four Russians who had already been living there for half of the 240 day period. The Russians and the group of foreigners did not stay together but were kept in separate compartments which were joined by a tunnel. On New Year's Eve, several weeks after the internationals had come in, things started going wrong. Two Russians started fist fighting. They were eventually separated and brought under control but the others, to be on the safe side, hid all the knives from the kitchen in case an outbreak escalated further. The situation was about to get out of control, but in a different way. One of the Russians found the Canadian participant, made sure they were out of range of the CCTV and tried to kiss her. Judith Lapierre, the Canadian woman, managed to push him away, but the morning afterwards the Russian harassed her again. There was a complaint to the experiment supervisors, but they disparaged the incident as trivial. Then the participants got an opportunity to express differences of opinions. Those who did not were asked to leave the experiment. The Canadian's behavior was found to be too saucy. Lapierre was the one blamed for the disturbance, had she given in, the situation would not have escalated. The international participants were not satisfied with this conclusion. The Japanese test participant decided to leave and was substituted with a Russian. Ten days after the incident, the door between the two groups was locked to prevent further incidents. Lapierre decided to stay till the end of the experiment. From inside her compartment, she informed her family of everything that was going on: about the harassment, cold showers, roaches and lice. That was not how she had initially imagined the experiment.

Several of the other isolation tests turned out to be a success. This was also true of other experiments that focused on acquiring information on the way the human organism adapts to conditions in space. For example, bed rest studies were conducted in the course of which a person had to stay in bed for months on end. It allowed scientists to study space symptoms, such as the weakening of muscles and bone decalcification. The psychological effects of such experiments were also looked into with great interest, because however easy it may seem, staying in bed in a horizontal position over a long period of time is in fact a very challenging task.

Carl Meade waves at the camera as he is lowered into the swimming pool where he will practice spacewalking. The underwater conditions are very similar to those experienced in a state of weightlessness; astronauts also experience the feeling of floating. The weight of an astronaut and his suit is set precisely so that he remains floating in the water: he goes neither up to the surface nor does he dive down to the bottom. However, an astronaut in water can still feel his own weight, which is not the case in space. Nevertheless, training sessions in swimming pools provide astronauts with a useful opportunity to get conditioned to working and moving around in their space suits. On Earth, it is not possible to simulate a long-term space mission: a zero-gravity state during a parabolic flight lasts merely tenths of seconds.

make one last trip into space. They were certainly not textbook athletes, those people. Many astronauts keep flying into their late fifties and sometimes even into their sixties. Some have flown as many as six times. You therefore do not need to be as fit as the first astronauts were.

In principle, anyone admitted to the astronaut corps is also granted work on a space mission at one time or another. There has been so much money and time invested in training people after all. Astronauts are often involved in the process of developing new equipment and in experiments for space shuttle missions. They can also fulfill the role of CapCom operators. Nevertheless, there are distressing examples of astronauts

Assisted by scuba divers, astronauts Takao Doi (from Japan) and Winston Scott, in a simulator of a space shuttle, try spacewalking in a swimming pool. The first Japanese, Doi carried out a spacewalk in 1997.

who had to wait more than ten years before they got their chance. Those who are assigned minor jobs on the ground after their space missions can be sure that their role is diminishing. However, space organizations never disclose the identity of those less successful astronauts. The presumption is that the differences at the top (and all those at the top made it through the immensely stringent selection process) are so minute that virtually everybody is fit and worthy.

French astronaut Jean-Francois Clervoy radiates joy while training for his space shuttle flight in May 1997. Up till this time, he had participated in three missions. Clervoy is in the service of the European space organization ESA.

Page 35:
Japanese astronaut Koichi Wakata looks up, during a parachute landing exercise in a swimming pool in Houston.

European astronauts Pedro Duque (Spain), Thomas Reiter and Ulf Merbold (Germany) and Christer Fuglesang (Sweden), in a swimming pool in Star City.

Those that want to explore space can chose to work in the American, the European or the Chinese space organizations. They are all linked to their respective governments. There can be disadvantages when political motives play a role in the selection. Currently, this is the case in Europe, where virtually every member state of the ESA wants to have its representative in space. Unfortunately there are not enough seats available, and this sometimes causes argument. In reality, the biggest countries get the most astronauts into space. Representatives from smaller countries often have to wait longer before they

get their chance. The suitability of an astronaut plays a minor role in this case; his passport seems to play the decisive role.

Things are rather different for scientists who wish to make a single journey into space. They are nominated by researchers involved in scientifically oriented missions. But it is NASA which offers such free seats aboard its space shuttle and which also understandably has the last word in the selection process. Even though things seem normal and cultivated to the outside world, the competition can become very severe and ruthless.

There are other avenues into space, however. Not everyone is willing to devote his or her life to carrying out a number of space missions. For several years now it has been possible to fly as a paying customer. Unfortunately, a ticket into space is very expensive. The person who wants to spend a week at the ISS

Who: *Walter Schirra*, USA
(1923)
What: *Apollo 7*
When: *1968*

Why: *Ewald was perhaps the most rebellious astronaut. During the Apollo 7 flight, Schirra's third mission, he suffered badly from a cold. He regularly complained that he and his two crew colleagues were being overburdened with work. He complained of sleep depravity, shortage of food and malfunctioning equipment. When the flight control made yet another change to the flight plan, Schirra decided it was too much. He refused any further changes in the already full agenda. From that point on he wanted to have a say in the mission planning. The other astronauts were also getting fed up with the situation. Once on the ground, they planned to have a word with those who made their lives so difficult. Nine months after the landing of Apollo 7, Schirra left NASA and took up a job in a commercial establishment.*

Page 37:
German astronaut Reinhold Ewald practices spacewalking in a pool in Star City. Ewald, in service of the European space organization ESA, spent eighteen days in the Mir orbital station in 1997 and witnessed, besides other things, a fire onboard the station.

Crew of Soyuz mission, scheduled fly to the ISS in April 2004, trains in a simulator of one of the Russian modules in Star City. In the background you can see Dutch astronaut Andre Kuipers, on the right, American Mike Fincke and in the foreground, Russian cosmonaut Gennady Padalka.

Page 39:
Astronaut Mike Foale gets ready to step into a Russian Orlan space suit in which he will try spacewalking.

must be able to pay some twenty million dollars. This amount is paid to the Russians who regularly offer a seat in their Soyuz capsule.

Several millionaires, such as American Dennis Tito and South African Mark Shuttleworth, have so far exploited this possibility. They received a short training which consisted mainly of lessons in Russian and emergency procedures. During the mission they were not allowed to touch a single control button aboard Soyuz or in the ISS but that after all was not their intention; they considered themselves tourists. Now and then they gave a helping hand but their main activity was hanging around. They enjoyed the views and horsed around in zero-gravity. And they bore very little resemblance to astronauts as we traditionally perceive them.

Faithful to the tradition, cosmonauts pay a visit to Red Square in Moscow prior to their space mission. Behind the Lenin Mausoleum, the grave of Yuri Gagarin is incorporated into the Kremlin wall. Sergei Krikalev, William Shepherd and Yuri Gidzenko are about to lay flowers at the grave in the run-up to their stay at the ISS in 2000.

Page 41:
Italian astronaut Roberto Vittori (in the foreground) and his Belgian colleague Frank de Winne photographed while exercising in a Soyuz simulator in Star City. Astronauts can use the brown straps to pull themselves up. It is not easy to get out of the crampea capsule interior with a space suit on.

Three inflated but empty Russian space suits left behind in seats

The opening of the cosmos for the masses is a long way away but the first steps have already been taken. In 2004, there were the first successful flights of a manned space ship built by a privately-owned company in the USA. Its name is SpaceShipOne.

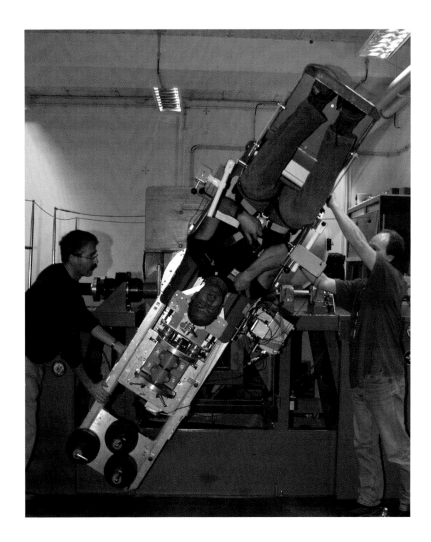

Astronaut Andre Kuipers spins around in the Dutch research institute TNO. During his flight to the ISS in 2004, he tested a vest designed at the TNO institute which allowed him to determine which way is up and which down.

The vessel made a brief jump to the outer rim of the atmosphere; an exceptional experience for the rich tourist who wishes to see a view of the Earth. It is widely expected that the intellectual and physical threshold for astronauts will further decrease. Professional astronauts will be hired for the tough jobs but perhaps there will be a number of passengers for whom a space flight will equal the simple act of writing out a fat check.

Page 43
Swedish astronaut Christer Fuglesang gets out of a Soyuz capsule underwater during survival training in Russia.

Leaving for Space

Leaving *for Space*

The launching of a spacecraft has always been surrounded by an aura of mystery and solemnity. Virtually everything and everybody service the people who risk their lives in a ginormous launch vehicle that transports them into the universe. For them, the day of the launch presents a point of culmination of the long-term preparations and extreme efforts. All that work is concentrated in one single moment that means a start to their space mission. Those who assist on the ground are well aware that no single error may occur. Everybody knows that one mistake is the difference between life and death.

As an example, let's look at the rubber insulation rings of space shuttle vehicles. In January 1986 the rings were damaged due to exposure to low temperature, and this resulted in the Space Shuttle Challenger exploding shortly after its liftoff. And think of the tragic accident of Columbia seventeen years later. At the start, a loose fragment of insulation material grazed the Shuttle's thermal shield, which consequently led to a disastrous explosion during the re-entry phase. Small

Before they go into space, cosmonauts traditionally visit the Baikonur Museum. Here you can see Salizhan Sharipov signing a special board prior to his space journey to the ISS station in 2004.

errors resulted in fatal consequences. The launch of a space rocket is an operation which must be carried out with military precision and discipline. The chaotic media circus pays little attention to the technical preparations and measures followed both in Russia and the United States according to painstakingly detailed preparatory plans.

The Kennedy Space Center has state-of-the-art technology that is somewhat taken for granted at a launch site. Baikonur in Kazakhstan, on the other hand, looks like a dilapidated industrial zone. The Kennedy Space Center is a prominent tourist site whereas Baikonur has until recently been a high security military terrain. Nevertheless, both sites have for decades now been producing similar ground-breaking achievements. Both sites have been gateways to space through which more than four hundred people have gone.

Several weeks prior to a rocket's launch, Russian cosmonauts move from the training center in Star City near Moscow to the Baikonur cosmodrome in Kazakhstan. The journey takes more than three hours by plane. Barren land stretches as far as the eye can see. Here and there are a few stray dogs and in the background sheep graze the Kazakh steppe. Twisted fragments of metal are scattered all over the grass. The only signs of civilization are the tall concrete and steel structures towering on the horizon. Those are the launching pads and assembly hangars which, in the past, were a great mystery to

To this day, cosmonauts visit a small cabin at the Baikonur cosmodrome in which Yuri Gagarin and Gherman Titov spent the night before the world's first space mission back in 1961. Inside is a bed in which Gagarin slept, as well as his uniform and his shoes. The experience is intended to emphasize the simplicity of socialistic cosmonauts: in the whole of the little house, there is no visible sign of luxury.

the American intelligence satellites. What was going on inside those immense halls? Baikonur dates back to 1956, but only a few years ago did the West get an opportunity to gain insight into what was happening there. Eventually, it became possible for foreigners to use the base as a launching site.

Baikonur is not only the name of a vast (50 by 60 miles) cosmodrome. The rundown city, which is approximately half an hour's drive from the base, is also called Baikonur. Most of the people who work at the site live in the town. In the center square, a statue of Lenin remains, steady and intact. The city does not give the impression of a comfortable or enjoyable place to live. It is hot in summer and freezing cold in winter.

Who: *Valentina Tereshkova,*
Russia
(1937)
What: *Vostok 6*
When: *1963*

Why: *Until March 1962, Tereshkova was employed as a worker in a textile factory in Yaroslavl. In her spare time, she went parachuting. Then she applied for a position as a cosmonaut and, to her great surprise, she was accepted. In June 1963 she became the first woman to spend three days in space. She was awarded the Medal of Heroism of the Soviet Union, two Orders of Lenin, the Order of the October Revolution, the Order of the Red Banner of Labor, the Order of Merit to the Country, Medal 'Gold Star' of Heroism of the Socialistic Labor of the People's Republic of Bulgaria, Order of Georgy Dimitrov, Grunwald Cross, Order of Nepal, Order of the Star of Indonesia, Order of Valta (Ghana), Order of the State Banner of Yugoslavia, Medal 'Gold Star' Hero of the Mongolian People's Republic, Order of Suhe-Bator (Mongolia), Order of Enlightenment (Afghanistan), Order of the Planet (Jordan), Medal 'Gold Star' Hero of Vietnam, Order of O'Higgence (Chile), Order of Yugoslavian Banner, Order for 'Progress in Science' (Rumania), Order of the Sun (Peru), Order Plaia Hiron (Cuba), Order of Anna Betankur (Cuba), High Order of Ethiopia, K. E. Tsiolkovsky Gold Medal of the USSR Academy of Sciences, a Gold Star of the British Interplanetary Communication Society, Gold Medal of International Aviation Federation, Gold Medal of the Globe in the name of Zholio-Kuri (France), Order of Windflower of Italy of the Italian Women Union, the Gold Medal of Freedom from the United Nations, the Gold Medal of Joliot-Curie and the Gold Medal of the Soviet exposition for economic achievements. On the dark side of the Moon, there is one crater which bears her name. Not to mention her honorary memberships, doctorates and cities that granted her their honorary citizenships.*

This picture shows a statue of Yuri Gagarin standing near the Baikonur Museum.

During the dry season, which is basically year-round, sand storms pass through the wide streets of Baikonur. Many apartment buildings are abandoned. The era of prosperity during which the complex was built in the sixties is long gone.
Cosmonauts never forget to visit certain historic sites at the base. One of these is the wooden log cabin which provided

Mike Foale (USA) Alexander Kaleri (Russia) and Pedro Duque (Spain) take time to wave to the press in October 2003.

Page 51:

Columbia leaves for a scientific mission in 1992. The propulsion of the spacecraft is provided mainly by two white booster rockets, the so-called Solid Rocket Boosters.

Yuri Gagarin and his replacement Gherman Titov with shelter the night before the world's first space mission. The cosmonauts go to the museum where they add their autographs to the others on a wall. The hotel where most of them lodge has a sort of auditorium separated by a wall of glass from a conference hall. Behind the glass, crews hold daily press conferences in the run-up to their launch. It always turns into

Space Shuttle: names and numbers

People sometimes do not realize that there is nothing quite like the space shuttle. In reality, they are a small fleet of Orbiters (airplane-like aircrafts where astronauts sit). Each time they are launched with a different fuel tank and propelling rockets. Parts of those propelling rockets (called Solid Rocket Boosters) are reused. The big brown fuel tank is lost at every liftoff and it is left to burn out in the atmosphere.

In total, five Orbiters have been built so far. The Enterprise Orbiter was used at the end of the seventies to test the landing of the space shuttle. The Orbiter has never been in space. The first shuttle to reach space, Space Shuttle Columbia, did so on April 12, 1981. Challenger, Discovery and Atlantis followed. Together they served for the numerous space shuttle missions. On average there were some fifteen space flights a year. When the Challenger was lost January 28, 1986, a new orbiter was assembled: the Space Shuttle Endeavor. Since the catastrophic destruction of the Columbia on March 1, 2003, only three orbiters have remained. This space fleet will not be further expanded with new shuttles because NASA intends to come up with a new type of spacecraft in due time which will eventually replace the Orbiters.

NASA is mad about abbreviations and so they started using the letters STS for Space Shuttle missions. This abbreviation stands for Space Transportation System. The Orbiters' flights are referred to as STS-1, STS-2 and so on. This counting was maintained only as far as STS-9, but by then it was clear flights would be organized in a more complex way. To avoid further confusions and misunderstandings, a new (from our current perspective much more complicated) manner of counting was introduced. NASA started to refer to missions with two digits and one letter. The first digit referred to the year of a given flight (for example 1984 was simply 4), the second digit referred to a particular launching site (1 was used to denote the Kennedy Space Center; 2 denoted Vandenberg Air Force Base launching site in California, at that time still under construction) and the final letter indicated when a given flight took place. To give an example, mission STS-41B stands for the second Shuttle flight in 1984, launched from Florida.

When it became clear that the launching site in California would never be completed – the Pentagon had lost its interest in space shuttle flights – the new coding became senseless. The old way of denoting STS missions was reintroduced after the crash of Challenger, the first mission after the accident was marked STS-26 simply because it was the twenty-sixth space shuttle mission. Since then, confusions have repeatedly occurred because one mission was delayed and a next was given higher priority and was launched earlier.

Russians maintain a rather different system. For them a flight number does not associate with a task or landing but denotes merely the chronology of launching. From Soyuz 1 on, flights have been numbered according to this simple rule. When a new module is introduced, for example Soyuz-T, a fresh count starting with number one begins. It happened when two new space module types were introduced: Soyuz TM and consequently Soyuz TMA.

a spectacle. Astronauts sit in their overalls next to their back-up colleagues. On the other side of the glass, sit photographers, journalists and cameramen. By means of a microphone and a sound system they can ask the space explorers questions, but due to the hectic atmosphere and constant blinding flashes, they hardly make any eye contact with the crew. Again and again the same questions are asked: how are the crew members feeling? is everything ready? and do they feel anxious to go?

Once the press conference is over, astronauts usually watch one particular movie together: "White Sun of the Desert", a Russian western from the seventies which is screened a night before liftoff into space. Nobody dares question this strange ritual. Some eight hours before the start, the crew leaves the hotel and gets on a waiting bus which takes them to the heart of the base. This is not something that would escape the attention of the media. First, the astronauts autograph the hotel door. Then they get a blessing from a Russian Orthodox priest. Then a moment of deep silence, with respect to the long journey they are about to set out on. They drink a glass of champagne, but they never propose a toast, which is said to bring bad luck. Then they come out, accompanied by a folk song roaring from loudspeakers. Surrounded by a crowd of applauding supporters they walk out of the main entrance of the hotel and take their seats on the bus. Once on

Italian astronaut Roberto Vittori and South-African Mark Shuttleworth check each other's space outfits prior to their Soyuz mission in April 2002.

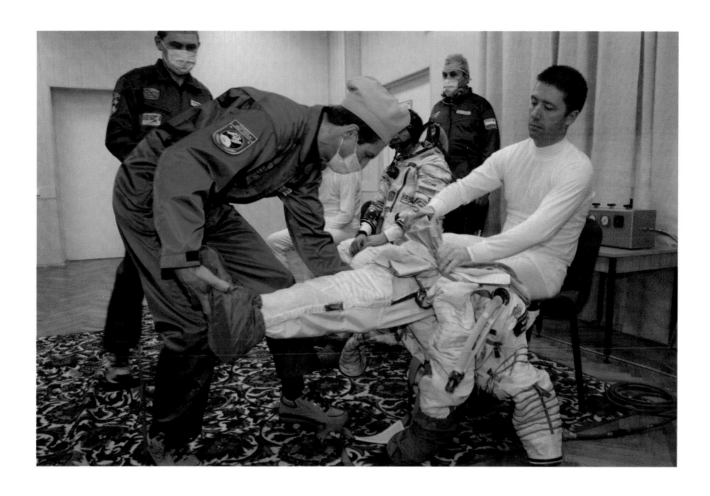

the bus they put a sticker with a flight insignia on a partition behind the driver.

And off they go across the barren land to the launch pads in a convoy escorted by flashing police cars. That is where the

Roberto Vittori is dressed for his space flight to the ISS.

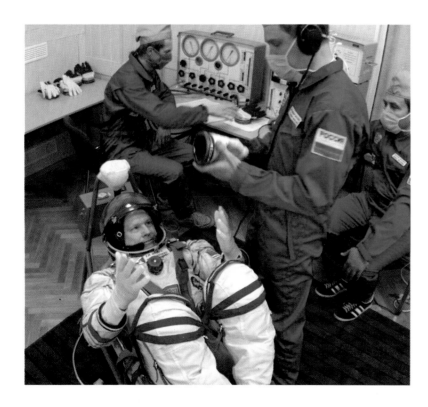

American astronaut William Shepherd gets his gloves put on during space suit preparations for his flight to the ISS in 2000. Shepherd is about to lift off in a Soyuz module with two Russian cosmonauts.

Page 55:
In April 2004, a Soyuz rocket leaves to the ISS
with one Dutch and two Russian astronauts
on board.

true liftoff preparations take place. They get into their space suits and have the air pressure tested in one of the numerous gray buildings. That as well happens behind a wall of glass and is observed by a hall full of dignitaries and press. Some VIP guests give speeches. Then the crew goes outside. There, in a kind of yard, they proceed to three marks which are painted white on a blacktop. Each astronaut has his own spot; the commander always stands in the middle. Opposite

Who: *Boris Volynov, Russia*
(1934)

What: *Soyuz*

When: *1969*

Why: Boris Volynov joined the Soviet Union space corps in 1960. But it took some time before he was allowed to fly to space. In 1963 he was selected for a space flight in a Voshkod capsule but one year later flights of this type of capsule were terminated. In 1966, Volynov was a member of a group of cosmonauts who started training for flights to the Moon, but this ambitious space program was also cancelled. Two years later, Volynov was nominated for a Soyuz flight, but the central committee of the Communist Party, which at that time endorsed all space flights, refused to approve Volynov because of his mother's Jewish roots. Eventually, Volynov did fly into space. His day came in January 1969. His landing became one of the most dramatic in the history of space exploration: during the re-entry phase, the landing module (with Volynov inside) did not separate completely from the rear part which, among others, contained the propelling engines. Both modules entered the atmosphere. Volynov's heat shield was oriented in a different direction than had been planned and everything around him started creaking and cracking under the enormous pressure. He could see the interior walls bowing inside. Then, all of a sudden, the couplings holding both modules together let loose and, at the last moment, Volynov managed to get his module into the right position. He landed one thousand five hundred miles from the calculated site of landing. Just before touchdown, the small supporting landing rockets (used to slow the last phase of the fall) did not ignite, which resulted in several lost front teeth.

Shortly after the flight, Volynov escaped death again when someone shot at the car in which he rode at the occasion of a parade in Moscow. The bullets were in fact intended for President Brezhnev, who rode in another car.

In 1976, Volynov made his second flight. After two months spent in the Salyut 3 space station, he had to return ahead of schedule because his colleague Vitali Zholobov did not feel healthy. In fact both cosmonauts were in bad shape because they paid little attention to keeping fit. But above all, they did not feel well emotionally: they were seriously homesick.

Shortly before the cosmonauts depart in the bus to the launching pad, the air pressure in their space suits is tested. This is done by inflating the suit with the astronaut inside. In the foreground, Dutchman Andre Kuipers sits in his bucket seat in exactly the same position as at launching. In the background, you can see American Mike Fincke and Russian Gennady Padalka. The whole is performed in a hall full of guests who watch from behind a wall of glass (not visible in the photo).

them, the chairman of the state commission for space exploration stands. The crew, at least those who are in the Armed Forces, salutes their commander who in turn declares the crew to be ready for the mission. They are surrounded by a crowd of journalists, family members and officials all pushing forward. They can hardly be kept within the white line. In a sea of flashes, the crew waves as the ceremony reaches its end. They walk a few meters to the waiting bus and board. Photographers and cameramen run after them and try to take pictures. The bus then drives away, once again followed by flashing police cars. The last thing to be seen is a horseshoe at the back of the bus hung there as a good-luck charm. The bus drives to the launching platform which is located several miles away. But it makes a short obligatory stop on the way; in April 1961, Yuri Gagarin got off the bus to take a pee against one of the bus' tires and since then every astronaut has followed his example and done just that–none of the female members of the crew, of course. Back in the bus, the space suits are tested again. Then they all go straight to the launch pad where astronauts see for the first time the launch vehicle which will take them into space. The rocket is transported the day before, at seven o'clock in the morning,

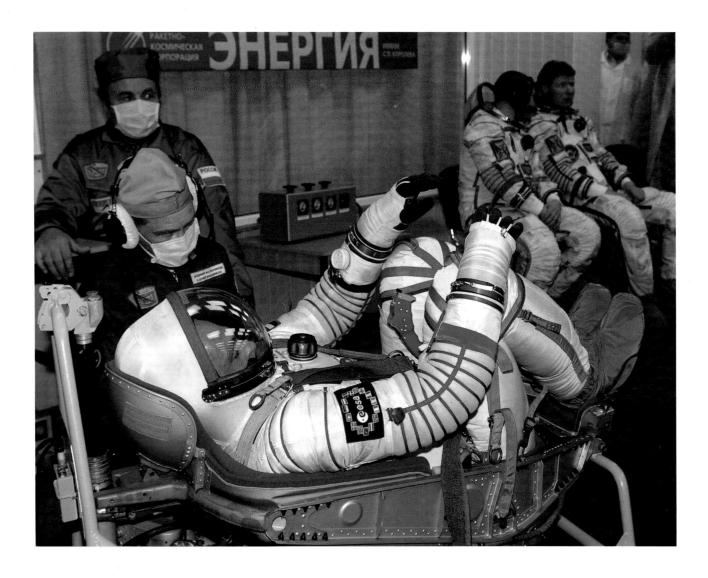

just as Gagarin's rocket was. The 140 feet tall goliath is transported in a horizontal position on a special railway wagon which is pushed forward by a rather small locomotive. Along the way, officials lay coins on the rails to see them flattened by the wagon later on: this ritual is also said to bring good

Cosmonaut Viktor Afanasyev and Claudie Haignere enjoy a private chat while getting dressed for their flight in October 2001.

Prior to the launch of every Russian mission, a priest of the Russian Orthodox Church gives the mission crew his blessings. American Mike Foale (left) and Spanish astronaut Pedro Duque watch as their colleague Alexander Kaleri receives the blessings.

luck to the mission. Once on the launch pad, the rocket is lifted into its vertical liftoff position and the fuel tanks are filled. When crew members approach the fuming and hissing rocket, it is time to say the last good-bye. As the tradition has it, no handshakes are allowed because this also might bring bad luck to the mission. The crew walks up one step, turns around and waves for the very last time. Then they step into the lift which brings them to the top of the launch vehicle. At last,

Names and functions

The French call their space explorers 'spationaut' and in China the word 'taikonaut' or 'yuhangyuan' is widely used. However, a member of the European space corps is by his employer referred to as an astronaut even if he comes from France and even if he flies with Russians.

Space shuttle crew members can be divided according to their functions into several groups. There is the commander who ranks above all others. During liftoff, the commander sits on the left side of the cockpit. He is also the one who takes over the spacecraft's controls in the last phase just before the touchdown and who in case of non-standard situations carries out the emergency landing procedures. The pilot sits next to him. He checks all onboard systems, such as thrusters, propelling rockets, main engines, hydraulic systems and the power supply. During takeoff and landing, the pilot is busier than the commander, who merely supervises the proper execution of the procedures.

Then there are always several mission specialists aboard the ship. They carry out tasks that have to be done during the mission: they for example carry out spacewalks; they operate the hydraulic arm (so called Remote Manipulator System or RMS) and carry out the planned experiments. Sometimes a loading specialist joins the mission. They are not professional NASA astronauts but external specialists who are assigned to execute certain specific tasks onboard. At times, there is for instance a medical doctor with the crew who takes care of medical experiments.

Aboard a Russian Soyuz module there is enough space for three persons. One of them is the commander who coordinates the routine operations. He sits in the middle. On his left sits the board engineer, who is responsible, among other things, for the module systems and the execution of flight procedures. To his right, there is a 'cosmonaut researcher' who checks certain systems according to the commander's instructions. This third seat is also for paying guests who are not allowed to touch anything during the flight. Cosmonauts are trained to fly and navigate the capsule on their own in case of a non-standard situation.

The ISS also has its own hierarchy even though currently, the station's crew consists of two astronauts only. One of them is the commander and the other is the ship engineer who at the same time carries out scientific experiments. This last function can be taken over by a third astronaut who usually stays on board for longer periods of time. The ISS commander also supervises the visiting astronauts on board the station. That means that a commander of a visiting crew is a subordinate. Inevitably, astronauts from different countries sometimes argue about who should hold the commanding position. One example: cosmonaut Vladimir Solovyev, one of the most experienced and capable Russian cosmonauts, refused to join an ISS mission because he was supposed to be subordinated to an American commander.

April 2004: Mike Flincke, Gennady Padalka and Andre Kuipers say goodbye to a crowd that has gathered on the main area of the Baikonur cosmodrome.

they are assisted into the confined interior of their Soyuz capsule.

Moments later the privileged spectators together with journalists arrive at the two watch-posts, simple wooden platforms with light roofing, located half a mile from the launch pad. There are television screens on which immediate family members can watch the first moments of the liftoff as experienced inside the capsule. In the distance, the rocket is held to the ground by immense steel grabs. An old woman who has witnessed decades of manned space launches at Baikonur walks around and sells snacks and drinks. You can hear voices behind a screen of noise through the loudspeak-

French astronaut Claudie Haignere photographed inside her space suit as it is pressurized.

ers: astronauts communicate with the flight control. Over all these sounds and noises, a song is played, chosen especially by the crew.

The precise time of liftoff is announced long before. And there is nothing that could change it. The start of a Soyuz rocket has never been postponed due to bad weather conditions. It can rain, hail, a storm can be raging above Baikonur, but the rocket will start no matter what. The media circus before the start is less dramatic than in America where the count-down is transmitted from loudspeakers. At a given moment someone in a bunker near the platform pushes a button and the rocket's powerful engines are ignited. 'Let's go!' the flight commander shouts inside the capsule. (Yuri Gagarin used the very same words.) The sound of the engines reaches the watchposts two seconds after you see the ignition flame underneath the rocket. With an immense roar the rocket lifts off into the sky above Kazakhstan. The flames are so bright that you can not look at them directly. Within several minutes the Soyuz launch vehicle is out of sight but cheered on by applauding guests on the observation platforms. Live pictures from the capsule can be viewed and soon it is possible to

Surrounded by supporters and by-standers, the mission crew (from left to right: South-African Mark Shuttleworth, Russian Yuri Gidzenko and Italian Roberto Vittori) bids formal leave to the chairman of the State Commission for Space Exploration. Commander Gidzenko declares the crew ready to complete their mission. In his left hand, he holds a box which provides air-conditioning for his space suit. As soon as they finish saluting they will get on a bus waiting for them outside that will transport them to the launch pad.

notice that the rocket has reached zero-gravity. Astronauts remain seated. They will have to spend two days in the confined space of the capsule as it flies towards the ISS station. Once they get there they receive a traditional Russian welcome gift: bread and salt. At that moment, the cosmonauts become space explorers.

As in Russia, in the United States much attention is paid to the well-being of the astronauts' families. After all, astronauts leave their families for weeks and sometimes even months. In reality, the families of the crew members spend lots of time together. Two weeks before the planned launch of a space shuttle, the spouses of the previous flight throw a party for the wives of the upcoming mission astronauts. It is a nice tradition; women who took part in the space mission are also welcome, but absolutely no men are allowed.

The crew arrives at the John F. Kennedy Space Center launch site in Florida three days before the scheduled liftoff. They do not arrive in their cars but fly in T-38 jet fighter planes from Houston, Texas. Their arrival is a much attended media event: the astronauts climb out, take their places at the microphone

Pulled by an old locomotive, a 140 foot tall Soyuz rocket moves slowly through the Kazakh steppe on its way to the launch pad located several miles away. The train is followed by a fire truck and cars with technical support staff. The transport is supervised by military personnel. In the United States, a space shuttle, together with its launch vehicle, is transported in a vertical position on a platform designed specially for this purpose. The same transportation technique was used for regular space rockets in the past.

A horseshoe is nailed to the back of a bus which transports cosmonauts to launching pads.

Page 63:
Nearly half of all the space missions launched by Russians were carried out in one or another type of Soyuz capsule. Even though the word Soyuz is usually associated with a launch vehicle of the same name (that is a booster rocket used for transporting Soyuz manned capsules into orbit), these days Soyuz rockets are mainly utilized for the launching of unmanned satellites into the Earth's orbit. Since 1966, more than 1600 launches have taken place with one or another Soyuz type rocket as the main launch vehicle. Ninety eight percent of those missions were successful. Every year, ten to fifteen Soyuz rockets are built and the majority is used for the launching of regular orbit satellites.

There are four propelling rocket engines at the foot of the Soyuz launch vehicle. Those burn out two minutes after liftoff and are consequently rejected from the main rocket's body. The debris falls down to the steppes of Kazakhstan. In the past, wrecks of the Soyuz rockets were not collected and were simply left where they had fallen. These days more attention is paid to clearing the debris from Kazakh nature areas. The main body of the rocket continues ascending skywards at immense speed and once all the fuel is burnt, the engines in the upper part of the rocket are ignited. They carry the load up into orbit. Once the shielded nose cone is disengaged, the last phase of the launch begins and the load is transported to its planned destination. Currently, the main goal of Soyuz rockets is the ISS located in orbit. The station is reached after approximately two days of orbital maneuvers.

and say a few words to the press and some high-ranking officials. There is yet another special gathering for the astronauts and their close family members organized twenty-four hours before the start. It takes place in a beach house located several miles from the space center and is owned by NASA.

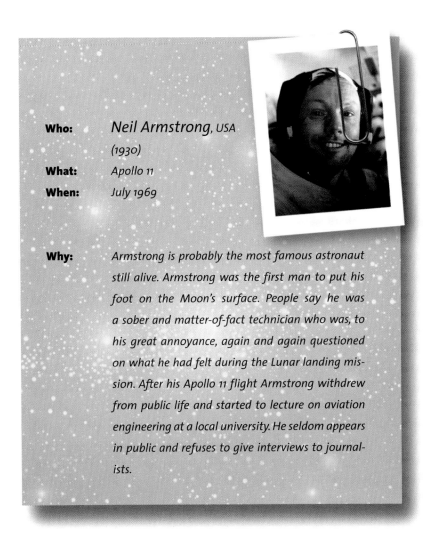

Who: *Neil Armstrong*, USA (1930)

What: Apollo 11

When: July 1969

Why: Armstrong is probably the most famous astronaut still alive. Armstrong was the first man to put his foot on the Moon's surface. People say he was a sober and matter-of-fact technician who was, to his great annoyance, again and again questioned on what he had felt during the Lunar landing mission. After his Apollo 11 flight Armstrong withdrew from public life and started to lecture on aviation engineering at a local university. He seldom appears in public and refuses to give interviews to journalists.

In April 2002, astronauts of a Soyuz flight wave to a crowd that has gathered in the vicinity of their launch vehicle. Below you can see Mark Shuttleworth, the South-African internet tycoon, who splashed out on his ticket to space and became the second space tourist ever – after American millionaire Dennis Tito. Above, Italian Roberto Vittori stands, in service of the European Space Agency ESA. Russian commander Yuri Gidzenko stands directly above. The cosmonauts are about to step into a lift which will take them to the top of the launch pad next to their rocket. Once there, they will be assisted into the Soyuz capsule.

The upcoming start of a space shuttle vehicle transforms the entire surroundings of the Kennedy Space Center which has been aptly nicknamed 'the Space Coast'. Good luck is wished to the astronauts on billboards along the roads. And everywhere you look there are souvenirs for sale: T-shirts, photos, mugs and flight insignia pins. The largest shop of all is located at the visitors' center of the Kennedy Space Center. True space enthusiasts can spend all the money they have. The hardcore enthusiasts park their mobile homes days before the planned launch in one of the many camping sites or camp anywhere along the long road. When an important mission is about to launch, neighboring places like Cocoa Beach and Titusville get slammed with traffic.

The crew does not see any of this however. They remain at the launch site. On the day of the launch the crew enjoys a light breakfast together at a long table in the middle of which is a cake with the flight's insignia. The cake is deep-frozen and saved for when the mission is over. Most astronauts make do with a sandwich and a glass of orange juice. This moment is much appreciated by the press for its symbolic and yet casual atmosphere. Then, as in Russia, a moment comes for reflections.

One of the most often discussed traditions of manned Russian space missions: ritual peeing on the front wheel of the bus; an intermezzo on the way to the launch pad.

The first man to try to shirk obligation was American astronaut Norman Thagard, who flew to the Mir station in 1995. He was afraid that he would be caught in the act on camera.

The Columbia stands on one of the two shuttle launch pads in Kennedy Space Center ready for liftoff in February 1996. In the background, is the Vehicle Assembly Building, the vast hangar for preparing first the Apollo and now the space shuttle launch vehicles. Below the launch pad, there is a deep concrete ditch which helps to avert the flames during ignition.

A space shuttle, in October 1992, leaves mountains of smoke and fumes behind after it lifts off from the launch pad.

The American astronauts are transported to the launching pad in a bus. Dozens of press people wait for them to board, cameras poised. This moment is called the 'crew walkout'. It is the last time the outside world will see them until they land safely. Security is everywhere: there are policemen with dogs and snipers are positioned on rooftops. Then, in one great explosion of camera flashes, the crew walks out. The astronauts wave, laugh and smile and now and then they shout something. This takes two minutes. Escorted by police, they are transported to one of the two launch pads. The astro-

Whoops...

There are advantages to having people in space instead of robots. Thanks to human interference many seemingly lost experiments were saved. It was only thanks to Neil Armstrong's powers of observation that the lunar landing module did not end up in a field full of cows. But people can also be the weakest link in the chain of causality. Here are some of the many recorded human errors in the history of space exploration:

– In May 1962, Mercury mission astronaut Scott Carpenter, at the beginning of his flight, accidentally engaged both the manual and automatic controls of the maneuver rockets six times, which resulted in an unnecessary loss of fuel. Later he lagged behind the schedule and this caused a delayed return. Carpenter ended up in the ocean hundreds of miles from the planned site of landing.

– In November 1969, Alan Bean accidentally focused the static camera on the sun. Because of this, no pictures exist of Apollo 12 astronauts moving around on the Moon's surface.

– In April 1972, while moon walking, John Young tripped over a cable laid by his colleague Charlie Duke on the Moon's surface. The cable was part of an important experiment which was not lost at the spot.

– In 1983, an astronaut drank a beer immediately after his return to Earth, which meant an end to a study of organ balance functioning.

– In July 1997, board engineer Aleksander Lazutkin accidentally disconnected the wrong plug in the Mir space station. The station consequently strayed from its course and temporarily lost electricity supply because solar panels were no longer oriented towards the sun.

– In October 1997, the undocking of a Progress cargo vehicle from the Mir station went wrong. The crew forgot to remove the docking mechanism. Eventually, they succeeded in properly undocking the cargo module but it took them one long hour.

– In November 1997, Indian astronaut Kaplana Chawla was operating the RMS (Remote Manipulator System or simply the hydraulic arm) of the Space Shuttle Columbia. She successfully moved the instrumental platform overboard. According to the plan, it was supposed to make one rotation so that its functionality could be checked. In the case it would not work out, Kaplana was given the task of taking hold of the platform by means of the RMS. Instead of taking hold of the platform she accidentally hit it; the platform began rotating uncontrollably and could not be grasped anymore. That had to be done later manually during an unplanned extra-vehicular activity (spacewalk).

– In October 2003, a cosmonaut aboard a Soyuz capsule, by pure accident, pressed two buttons at the same time. The action resulted in ignition of the module's engine a moment later. The only problem was that the capsule was at that time still attached to the ISS station. As a result of the heavy impact the station went off course. Fortunately, it was possible to maneuver the station back into its proper position and the Soyuz capsule eventually made a safe landing.

Launch pad 39-A at Kennedy Space Center, with Space Shuttle Endeavor in the middle, readies for its start in January 1998. The area around the launch pad must be cleared before the start. Unauthorized people are not allowed within three miles of the launch pad. The unique swamps around the center are swarming with alligators.

nauts step into the lift which takes them up to the top of the metal towers beside their space shuttle vehicle. The last checks are carried out in the white room, a small structure at the end of the transport arm on top of the launch pad. There are technicians waiting to check that everything is correct and assist with boarding the spacecraft. The liftoff takes place several hours from this point. At that time no one is allowed within three miles of the launch pad.

Launching procedures differ in one important aspect from those in Kazakhstan: loud counting can be heard, the so-called countdown. For example: 'T minus nine minutes!' barks the voice from loudspeakers when the start is nine minutes

away. Journalists stand on a wooden platform. The prepared space shuttle can be seen far away on the horizon, in the middle of the green swamps where the launch site is located. From the launch pad to the observatory platforms, there are

The crew of the STS-45 Space Shuttle mission arrives in a T38 fighter jet plane (in the background) at Kennedy Space Center to get ready for the liftoff. The commander – in this case Charlie Bolden, with the microphone – addresses the expectant press. One of the astronauts is Belgian citizen Dirk Frimout, second from the left. His main task will be to carry out scientific experiments onboard the spacecraft.

Several days before the start of the twenty sixth space shuttle flight – the first mission after the tragic crash of the Challenger – astronauts are greeted by their spouses shortly after they have landed at the Kennedy Space Center.

Page 71:

Space Shuttle Columbia rockets skywards above a cloud cover in Florida in November 1982. It is the very first mission of a space shuttle. Two satellites were later unloaded from the payload bay and put into orbit. It was also the first time four people were aboard one shuttle. The photograph was taken from a jet fighter plane.

The launch of Space Shuttle Challenger on October 30, 1985, with eight astronauts aboard, which is a record unparalleled to this day. Among them there are two Germans and a Dutch astronaut.

alligators, armadillos and birds of the wild. The whole area would be a nature reserve if this was not the United States. There is a man-sized digital clock in front of the press area where you can follow the countdown. Next to it, there is a big flagpole with the 'Stars and Stripes' at the top. Several hundred feet to the left, there is the immense Vehicle Assembly Building (VAB), the building which was used for assembling the Apollo rockets back in the sixties and which now prepares space shuttles for the missions. Several days before the start, the rocket emerges from the building. It is not transported on a train as it is in Kazakhstan, but on a crawler, an impressive caterpillar-tracked vehicle which has long been the biggest of its kind in the world. It moves at a very slow pace in the direction of the launch pad. Just as in Kazakhstan, the roll-out procedure at the Kennedy Space Center gets lots of attention.

The family members of the astronauts watch the liftoff from the roof of the control center which is located next to the VAB. The actual launch of the shuttle rocket is an impressive sight even from a relatively long distance. A voice on a loudspeaker counts down the last ten seconds: ten, nine,

eight...Reaching zero, the voice commands: 'Ignition!' and the engines are ignited. As with Soyuz, you can not only see and hear the departure of the space shuttle but you can feel it too. The vibrations can be felt in every fiber of your body. If the weather is clear you can see how both white booster rockets separate once they burn out. Afterwards, the rocket quickly disappears out of sight. The families go to have a chat over a traditional meal of bean soup and corn.

The launch of Space Shuttle Endeavor in September 1994. During the flight, radar pictures were made for environmental research purposes.

The launch is an incomparable experience for the astronauts. At the moment the engines ignite, a powerful shock penetrates the whole of the rocket. The space shuttle shakes and trembles and accelerates with immense power. The astronauts experience a maximum 4G at the liftoff; that is four times the acceleration of gravity. It feels as if you are four times heavier than usual. You breathe with more difficulty and your limbs get much heavier. The start is usually compared to a ride in a roller coaster but without the nasty curves. In contrast to what most people think, there is not much for the crew to do during liftoff. Everything is fully automatic; it is the computers that do all the work. The only button the shuttle commander needs to press is the adjustment of the altimeter. The commander and the pilot who sit next to each other in the cockpit have one major task: to check that everything works as it should. In case of emergency they must intervene; they have spent countless hours drilling non-standard situations. One scenario anticipates emergency landing on an airport on the other side of the Atlantic, in Spain or Morocco for instance. There are no ejection seats, nor parachutes. The Shuttle flies too fast for the crew to be able to leave it safely.

Astronauts of the STS-65 mission walk towards the so-called Astrovan, a bus which will transport them to the launch pad located several miles away. The flight served mainly scientific purposes. There was a whole laboratory in the payload bay in which experiments were carried out. The walk-out is the last opportunity to take pictures of astronauts before they leave Earth. Security measures around this event are very tight.

For a long time, Story Musgrave (in the middle of the front row) was one of the most charismatic American astronauts. He had six space shuttle missions. In 1991, during a general test launch, his crewmates poked fun at his baldness. Here, they are walking to the astrovan which will take them to the launch pad.

If everything goes according to plan, the space shuttle leaves the Earth's orbit in less then ten minutes. At the moment when the engines switch off, everything aboard the ship is in a zero-gravity state. If you look outside you can see the curved horizon between pitch-black space and the colorful

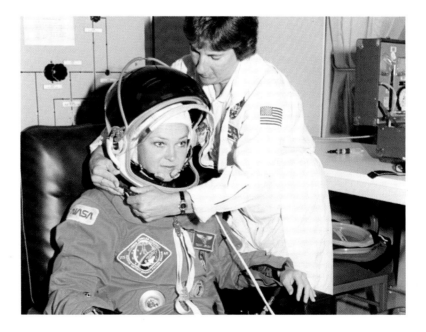

Astronaut Tammy Jernigan gets into the space suit in June 1991. Jernigan has been on board five space shuttle missions. She is married to another astronaut, Jeff Wisoff.

Earth. Many people have become astronauts only to be able to enjoy this breathtaking view. And to be able to float around, of course. The ship circles the Earth at a speed of 18,000 miles per hour, not being hindered by air resistance of any significance. Within thirty minutes the astronauts will have finished their first full orbit around the Earth.

Splendidly lit by surrounding spotlights and by the nearly full Moon overhead, the Space Shuttle Endeavor stands ready on the launch pad, in November 2002.

Life in Space

At present, space exploration efforts are concentrated around the International Space Station (ISS). Its assembly began in 1998. It is a project carried out in cooperation with a number of countries: the United States, Russia, most of the countries of the European Space Agency (ESA), Japan and Canada. During the first three years of the existence of the ISS community, it had to use a different orbital station: the Russian Mir which had been orbiting Earth since 1986. In 2001, Mir's existence was terminated by letting it fall apart above the ocean.

The ISS orbits the Earth at an altitude of approximately 240 miles. Once the station's assembly is finished, it will have a living area of some 42,377 cubic feet and it will weigh 419 tons. The date of its finalization is not yet clear. The project has so far been complicated by many factors. A lack of financial means resulted in certain modules, such as the living compartment, to be aborted. In reality, the station's crew lives in its working quarters just like in previous space stations. The major stumbling block on the road to the station's completion was the crash of the Space Shuttle Columbia in 2003. The Columbia was used to transport modules of the station into orbit. The Russian Soyuz and cargo rocket Progress can transport only people (currently a maximum of three) and rather small amounts of material and supply. After the unfortunate crash of Columbia, the assembling of the station had to stop temporarily. Various modules are now waiting to be transported into orbit, such as the European Columbus and the Japanese Kibo module. Both will be used for scientific research. In its current state, the ISS consists of Russian and American modules.

Russians do not use their small Soyuz capsules for long-term stays in orbit. Soyuz modules served merely as space taxis flying to Mir in the past and nowadays, mainly to the ISS. Before it became possible to stay over for longer periods of time in the ISS, American astronauts had to rely on shorter (one to two weeks) missions in their space shuttles. During recent decades, work and life in space took place in three different space vehicles: in the Mir, in the ISS and in space shuttles.

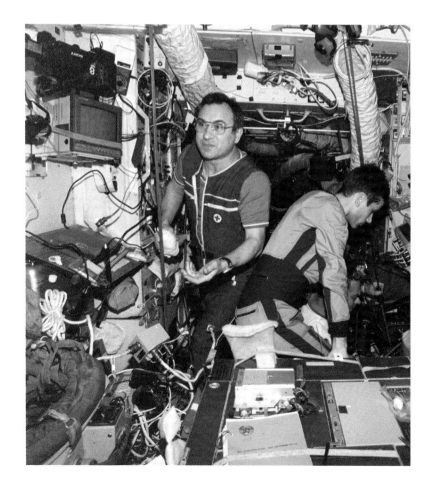

This photo shows cosmonauts Valeri Polyakov (left) and Yuri Malenchenko in the central living compartment of the Mir station. The picture was taken in 1994. During that mission, Polyakov was busy achieving the record period of time in space; eventually the physician managed to stay in space for 437 days in a row.

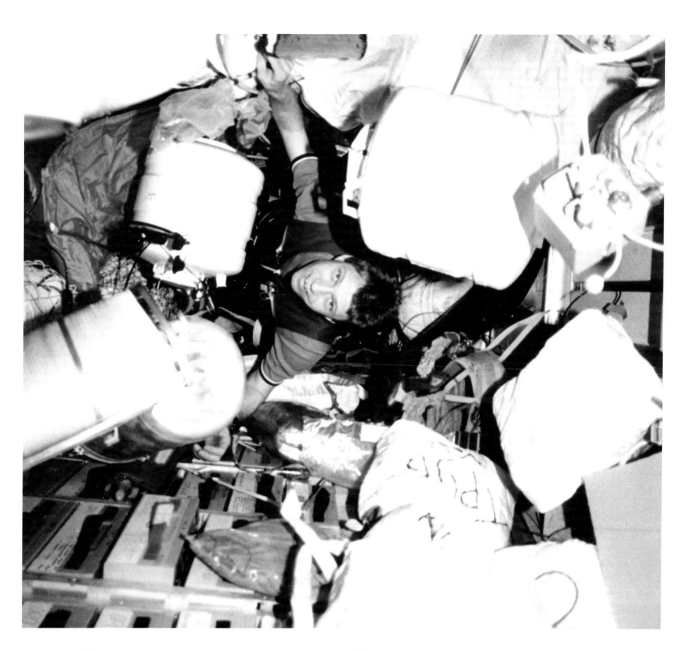

It is something you have to know you want: months of living in your workplace; not being able to go out for a walk; not being able to open a window; no visits to your local pub with friends; no sex.

Even despite all this, most astronauts desire only one thing once back on Earth, and that is to go back to space. There are people who have made five, six and even seven flights in their lifetimes. Some of them spent as many as two years of their lives in a space station. They willingly exchange their earthly existence for this unparalleled experience. A submarine crew has better equipment on board and on a South Pole base you can at least get some really fresh air. Nowhere else is the contrast to daily life on Earth as large as on a space station. And that is precisely why some people are so strongly attracted to the idea of orbiting the Earth. They want to float in zero-gravity and observe the Earth from space. These childhood dreams lead to a career for many an astronaut.

In the sixties, during the time of the first space flights, the main issue was to find out if people were capable of surviving in

There is almost not enough space for German astronaut Thomas Reiter to float around; such is the mess onboard the Mir station where he worked in service of the European Space Agency ESA in 1995.

Page 81:

American astronaut Steve Oswald is dressed in the pilot's seat of the space shuttle. He is dressed in the 'Launch Entry Suit' (LES) which is worn by astronauts during the launch and landing phase. Oswald served as pilot in two space shuttle missions and as commander in the third. He is no longer in NASA service.

Crew members of the ISS pose for a group photo. Most of them are visiting astronauts who will stay only shortly. The standard crew on the station currently consists of two people.

space. Would they survive the zero-gravity state? And what about the weird space radiation? Or would they get crushed as early as during the liftoff? Yuri Gagarin made only one orbit around the Earth back in 1961. The fact that he survived gave clear proof that the human organism was capable of functioning in space. In the following years, there was little or no attention paid to the astronauts' comfort levels. They often spent days sitting crammed in a capsule that was hardly bigger than a phone booth, caught in a space suit and completely surrounded by the capsule's controls. Space was not a place for living at that time. Being in space was purely a matter of survival. But the need to stay in space over longer periods soon became an issue of importance. To break a time-in-space record became a question of honor, especially in the former Soviet Union. When it became evident that Russians had lost the race to the Moon, they focused their efforts on living in a space station in orbit. Between 1971 and 1982, seven Salyut rockets were launched one after another. Salyut was as big as a mobile home. Two to three cosmonauts were usually inside and were at times visited by cosmonauts who stayed only for a short time. They traveled to and from Salyut space station in Soyuz

capsules. The permanent crew was usually replaced after several months. Astronauts could really float in Salyut and for the first time, a comparison could be made between life on Earth and in a space station. The walls of Salyut were also all covered with controls, switches and buttons; however, there was at least some space for moving around. Cosmonauts spent most of their days carrying out experiments in the field of material physics, physiology and biology.

In those years, Americans also maintained their own space station. At the beginning of the seventies, three groups of astronauts spent months in a row in Skylab which was partly built

Female (un)friendly

It did not take long for the Soviets to send the world's first woman into space. Valentina Tereshkova, a textile factory worker who devoted her free time to parachute jumps was selected to become the unique record holder in 1963. However, it was not until 1982 that the second Russian woman was sent into space. Why did it take so long? Most male cosmonauts pointed out the fact that for a female there was simply no suitable job in space. However archaic it may sound, the common perception of that time was that a woman's place was at home with children. And above all, a female interfered with the male culture which at that time dominated space exploration.

There were plans for sending more Russian female astronauts into space. Together with Tereshkova, other women were selected all of whom could fly without any difficulty. Later on, they continued to select suitable women for space missions. There were even daring plans to organize a mission with an all-female crew. But all in all, Svetlana Savitskaya in 1982 and 1984 and Elena Kondakova in 1997 remained the only ones. Kondakova is the wife of cosmonaut Valery Ryumin who, more than once, openly commented on the work of his wife. He in fact liked to see her at home. There are no indications that female cosmonauts would be less appreciated than their male colleagues but the prevailing attitude towards female cosmonauts in the Russian space community was not always truly friendly. This does not mean that foreign female astronauts have ever had any reason to complain of a lack of hospitality on board Russian space stations. No reports are known of protests of any sort against, for instance, the presence of American Shannon Lucid in Mir, who stayed on board the orbital station for 188 days.

In the American space corps, gender is no longer much of an issue. Women are adequately represented in the space corps and get regularly assigned to mission lists. The first American woman in space, Sally Ride who flew in 1983, attracted enormous attention. She was an African-American and at the same time, the first ever female commander of a space shuttle mission. However, after this groundbreaking event, a female presence in orbit was no longer perceived as an issue. Before this time, astronauts had to be experienced test pilots and women were in principle not allowed into this elite club. They were thus ruled out by the very selection criteria. That did in fact put off a number of female pilots who never even bothered to apply.

Members of the 'Fellow Lady Astronaut Trainees' (FLATs), with Jerry Cobb and Jacqueline Cochran as its most famous members, seemed to meet the same psychological and physiological requirements that were expected from male astronauts of that period – and sometimes they managed to get even better results. The FLATs never got a chance to prove their abilities in space however.

from parts that were transported by Saturnus 5, a rocket which was designed to take people to the Moon. Afterwards, Americans focused completely on the space shuttle, a space vehicle used to transport space labs into space and also frequently used for satellites maintenance jobs. A partially reusable shuttle launch vehicle was designed to take astronauts to and from permanent stations. The first flight of the new

The crew of the STS-26 Space Shuttle mission in 1988: they salute in the direction of a tracking station located on Hawaii.

Elena Kondakova is warmly welcomed back by her husband, cosmonaut Valery Ryumin.

Astronaut John Blaha plays handball during a space shuttle flight in November 1989. Blaha stayed on board Mir for several months.

spacecraft was launched in 1981 and there have been more than one hundred flights of the five orbiters: Columbia, Challenger, Discovery, Atlantis and Endeavor. A space shuttle can spend, at the very most, several weeks in a row in space. We cannot therefore talk of permanent stays in space of any sort. Still, a space shuttle is quite well equipped with a galley, toilet

Page 85:
Astronaut Rick Linnehan stretches his muscles aboard Spacelab in the payload bay of Columbia in summer, 1996.

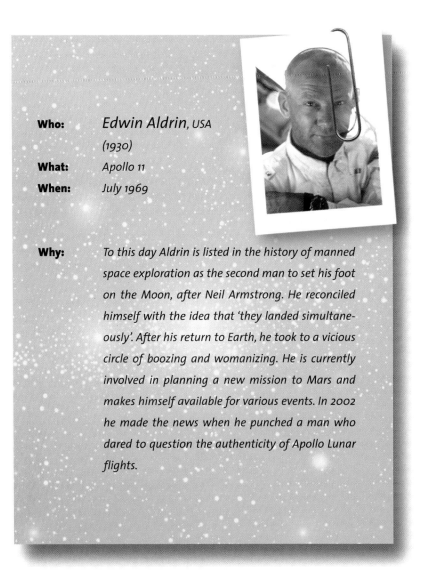

Who:	*Edwin Aldrin*, USA
	(1930)
What:	*Apollo 11*
When:	*July 1969*

Why: *To this day Aldrin is listed in the history of manned space exploration as the second man to set his foot on the Moon, after Neil Armstrong. He reconciled himself with the idea that 'they landed simultaneously'. After his return to Earth, he took to a vicious circle of boozing and womanizing. He is currently involved in planning a new mission to Mars and makes himself available for various events. In 2002 he made the news when he punched a man who dared to question the authenticity of Apollo Lunar flights.*

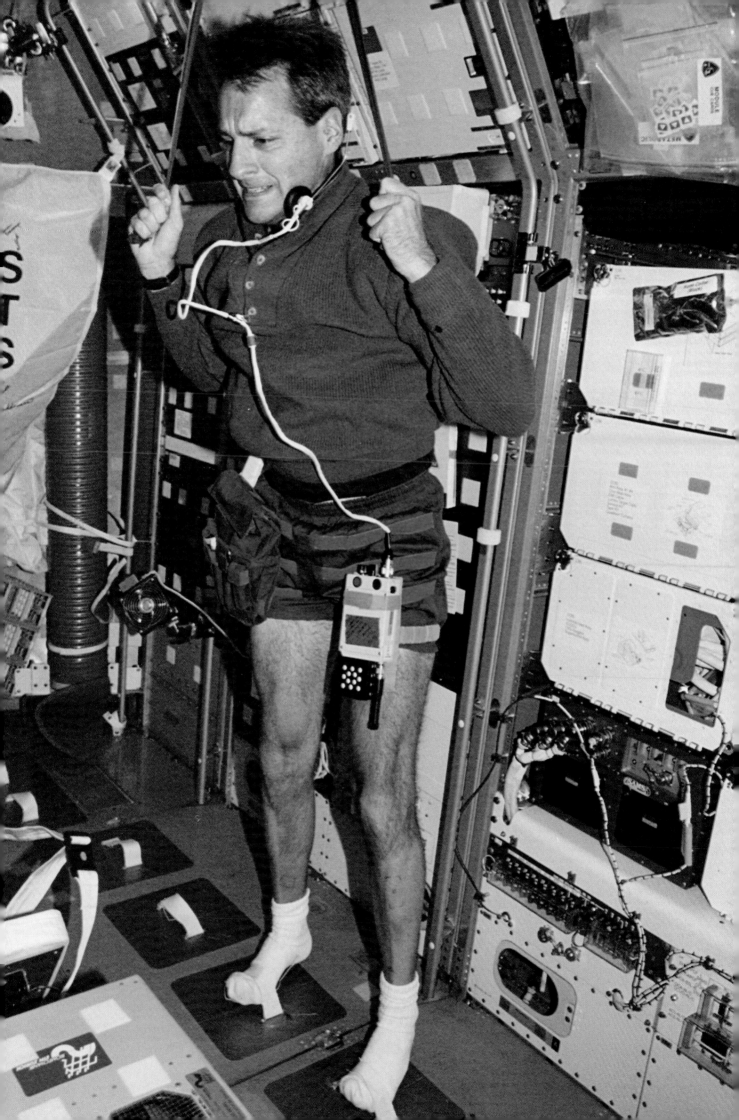

and sleeping quarters. In most cases, there are five to seven astronauts on board a space shuttle. Besides the professional NASA astronauts, at times there are scientists on board to carry out a range of specialized experiments. Nevertheless, the future of the space shuttle is quite uncertain. Since the Challenger exploded shortly after its launch in the eighties, there are no 'laymen' or paying guests allowed on board shuttle launch vehicles. It is still not clear how many more guidelines will have to be introduced following the crash of Columbia, which exploded during its landing. There certainly will not be as many as five flights per year as had been normal before the last shuttle accident.

Temporary stays aboard space shuttles can hardly be perceived as living in space. Certainly not when we compare with what Russians have so far achieved in this respect. In 1986 they launched into orbit their Mir space station which was permanently inhabited for fifteen years. Mir was considerably bigger than the old Salyut; there were even special compartments and

Under normal circumstances luxuriant, the hair of astronaut Marsha Ivins seems even thicker thanks to zero-gravity effect. Ivins has so far made five shuttle flights.

Page 84:
Astronaut Donald Petitt exercises on a home trainer on board the ISS.

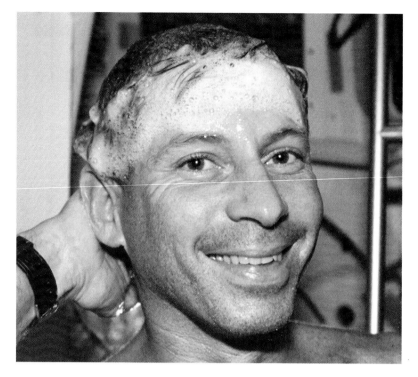

Space shuttle commander Kenneth Cockrell washes his hair in zero-gravity. He uses a special shampoo which is also used in hospitals and does not require much water. There are actually no showers, neither aboard Space Shuttle Orbiters nor in the ISS station. Astronauts wash themselves by means of wet towels. A long hot shower is very often one of the first things astronauts crave after they return to Earth.

modules equipped for scientific purposes. Many astronauts stayed there for shorter or long periods of time. The record stay in space was indeed achieved on Mir: 437 days spent there by physician Valeri Polyakov. Quite regularly, international guests were welcomed aboard the station (as paying guests they

Sex in space

When men and women spend time together in a confined place, sooner or later the topic comes up. The idea of sex in space naturally appeals to people's imaginations. Those who examine the given circumstances must inevitably come to the conclusion that the chance of something really happening up there is very small. There is simply so little privacy in a space station that sex between two people would be a rather embarrassing experience for all parties involved. After all, a man and a woman are never alone on board a station; there is always at least a third person there. It is virtually impossible for two people to find time for each other. Even if an opportunity occurs, either the man or the woman is working different shifts. There have been cases of couples together in space but they have just never got the chance as far as we know. There is nothing known of homosexuality among astronauts.

If you pose a question to NASA on the topic of sex in space the answer you most probably will receive is that sex is simply not on the agenda of space exploration. There has not yet been a researcher who would consider sex in zero-gravity a theme worth examining. However, it will become an issue worth researching once manned people are sent to Mars. Such a journey will take two to three years. Astronauts who spent longer periods of time in space were asked repeatedly how they felt about meeting their sexual needs. Well, there is an option, and that is masturbation, was the most common answer. Sex in space is not that mysterious a topic.

could usually stay a week or so). In previous years, Russians and Americans organized flights to Mir together. There was a political lesson to be learnt: the mutual projects of the once great enemies proved that they could cooperate in space better than they had on Earth. This will be necessary in the future because the maintenance of a space station has turned out to be way too costly for one country. There were also perilous situations aboard Mir: a fire, malfunctioning oxygen generators, on board computer malfunction, a critical collision with a Progress cargo rocket and the accidental unplugging of a system which rendered the station unstable. Eventually in 2001, Mir met its fate in the Pacific Ocean.

At that point in time, the United States, Russia, Europe, Canada and Japan were already concentrating their efforts on a new and highly ambitious mutual project: the International Space Station or the ISS. A name that would be acceptable for all involved parties has never been settled on. The first parts of the ISS were launched into orbit in 1998 and basically all flights of Space Shuttle and Soyuz have since then had one goal only: fur-

Dutch astronaut Wubbo Ockels photographed while conjuring 'an egg of Columbus' during his space mission in November 1985. This refers to the future contribution of Europe to the ISS – the European experimental module will bear the name Columbus – and with the trick he is trying to show that you can in fact put an egg upside down without making a dent in the egg.

American astronaut Ed Lu plays keyboard in the ISS. This photo shows that the station's interior looks most of all like an engine room. The worst source of frustration for those on board is the fact that they are always looking for things. It is an unbelievable mess and ever-present tangle of cables and wires.

ther assembly and habitation of the station. The ISS, once complete, will be as big as two soccer fields combined: it will be a maze of cylinder-shaped modules put together, of supporting structures and solar panels. The total costs might mount up to 600 billion USD which makes it the most expensive technological project ever. It is however not clear yet when the station will be complete. The assembly schemes and schedules had to be cancelled after the crash of Space Shuttle Columbia.

Page 91:
Astronaut Ellen Ochoa, a fanatic flute player, plays for her colleagues in Space Shuttle Discovery in April 1993.

Cosmonaut Gennady Strekalov strums his guitar in the Mir station in 1995.

Astronaut Carl Walz gives his ISS crewmates a mini concert on the keyboard which has been part of the station's inventory for years. Walz is also the lead singer of the astronauts' music band 'Max Q'.

Page 93:
German astronaut Thomas Reiter tests a collapsible guitar which has been brought in by the space shuttle crew. In the background there is a floating guitar that has been in the Mir for years.

Two things strike you when you look into the interior of the International Space Station. The first is the enormous chaos all around. There are cables lying everywhere, papers posted on the walls, equipment with myriads of controls, switches and screens. Music from the loudspeakers gets mixed with the screeching and peeping of machinery. More than anything else, the ISS is a workplace; that much is clear. It looks like one big engine room. It also smells like machines there, the air is filled

Falling around the world

How come astronauts float in space? Floating is not the right expression; strictly speaking astronauts fall. They fall but they can not feel it. Imagine you are standing in an elevator: someone on the top floor of a skyscraper cuts the lift cable. And down you fall. But the lift itself is also falling. And so are the weights. Everything is falling. Your body does not exercise any pressure and the indicator on the scales shows that you weigh nothing. We must presume of course that the elevator cage does not meet any air resistance during the fall.

But astronauts do not fall down, they fall around the Earth. They are pulled by speed which is too high to smash them down, and at the same time too low to shoot them away into the universe. In other words, the trajectory of their spacecraft has the same bent as the Earth. Theoretically, a spacecraft can keep moving on the trajectory forever because there is no air resistance. In practice, there are always some aerial particles that slow the spacecraft down causing it to descend gradually. There are more and more aerial particles and so a station goes down faster and faster. Orbiters moving in a flight level of several hundred miles above the Earth (and that applies also to all space stations) must therefore be 'jacked up' by thrusters from time to time. They increase the speed of the station and it ascends by means of the momentum. Once you let a spacecraft begin its descent back to the Earth it regains its speed very quickly.

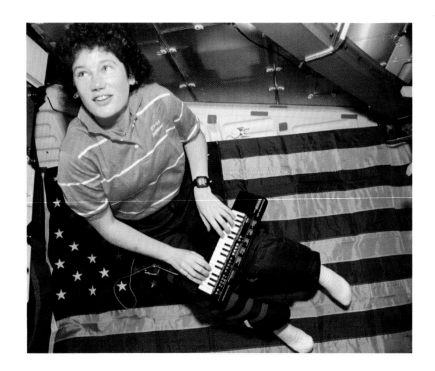

Astronaut Susan Helms plays keyboard onboard Space Shuttle Endeavor in 1993.

with the smell of metal and oil. It is definitely not a very inviting place to live at first sight. Every square inch of the interior is utilized. There are photos hanging here and there, but there can be no talk of a comfy atmosphere of any sort.

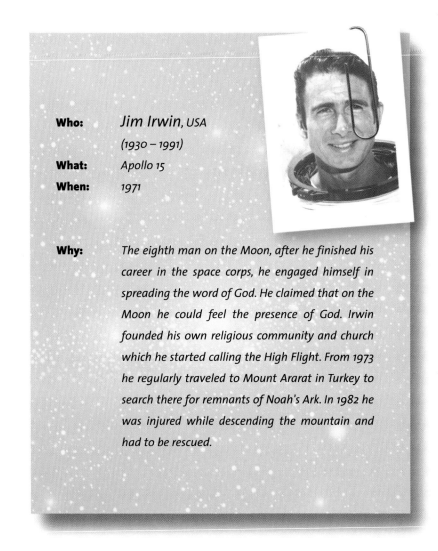

Who: *Jim Irwin,* USA
(1930 – 1991)
What: *Apollo 15*
When: *1971*

Why: *The eighth man on the Moon, after he finished his career in the space corps, he engaged himself in spreading the word of God. He claimed that on the Moon he could feel the presence of God. Irwin founded his own religious community and church which he started calling the High Flight. From 1973 he regularly traveled to Mount Ararat in Turkey to search there for remnants of Noah's Ark. In 1982 he was injured while descending the mountain and had to be rescued.*

The other strange aspect is that people do not walk but they float in the air instead. They lean against a wall and move along it to the other side of the station. They whiz like super-heroes through the interconnected compartments; they perform summersaults without touching the floor. There is no up or down. The consequences are immense. The main advantage is that the space inside can be more efficiently used. You can use ceilings to put things away or to help yourself move along.

Astronauts Frank Culbertson (right) and Daniel Bursch clean their teeth in Space Shuttle Discovery in 1993. It is important not to open your mouth too much because you then will have drops of tooth paste floating all around you.

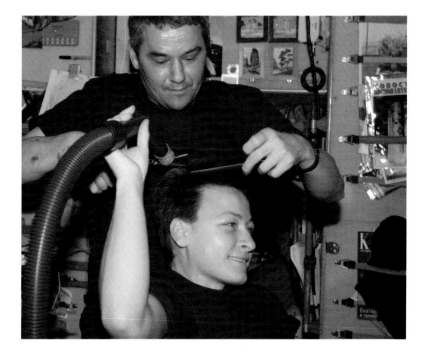

Cosmonaut Valery Korzun cuts the hair of his American colleague, Peggy Whitson. With a vacuum device he gets rid of the loose hair so that it does not float around everywhere.

Your sense of orientation is sometimes challenged to the limit. You would agree that it is a strange feeling to do a handstand and to see the room upside down. But in a space station you have to get used to seeing the interior from all possible angles. Greenhorns have to spend some time finding their way around. To give the astronauts at least some sense of direction, the floors are distinguished from ceilings (which are equipped with lights). There are rails everywhere which you can hold with your hands or hook with your legs if you need both hands. Still, you will end up with aching feet and calloused skin.

Zero gravity does not leave the human body unaffected. Feelings of disorientation make more than half of all astronauts space sick. Vomit bags therefore have to be at hand. This 'Space Adaptation Syndrome' can become even more annoying during a short mission because the flight is usually over just when the body has started to adapt.

Another effect of long stays in a state of zero-gravity can be felt especially in the lower back. Because gravitation no longer holds the backbone together, it naturally begins to stretch out. Astronauts can grow several inches longer a day or two after arriving in space. This comes with fierce pain of the back muscles which have to stretch out together with the vertebral col-

Astronaut Ed Lu eats in a 'living room' on board the ISS. He sits at a collapsible eating table; next to him is a machine used for preparing meals. The photos behind him show Russian space pioneer Konstantin Tsiolkovsky and Yuri Gagarin. Below is the interconnecting corridor which leads to another module of the station.

umn. Generally speaking, muscles are much less needed in zero-gravity; they are no longer necessary for walking, running or lifting weights. The result is that they weaken considerably and therefore daily space station routine involves regular fitness exercises. There is a runner and a home trainer. Arm muscles are trained with tension springs.

The bridegroom Yuri Malenchenko

Getting married in space

This is something special: a bridegroom whizzing around the Earth at the speed of more than 18.000 miles per hour during a wedding ceremony. On September 10, 2003, cosmonaut Yuri Malenchenko and his bride Yekaterina Dmitriev said the solemn 'I do' to each other. Malenchenko was somewhere above New Zealand; Dmitriev was sitting in a restaurant in Clear Lake, Texas. They could see each other on a TV screen. The ceremony was conducted by a lawyer. Texas legislation makes such long-distance wedding ceremonies possible. At a given moment, the bride and bridegroom simultaneously put on their wedding rings (Yuri's was brought by a cargo ship some time prior to the ceremony). Dmitriev was dressed in white, Malenchenko had a necktie on. American astronaut Ed Lu, the bridegroom's witness and crewmate on board the station, played a wedding song on his keyboard.

Malenchenko and Dmitriev had met each other six month earlier in 'The Outpost', a pub adjoining a restaurant close to Johnson Space Center which is frequented by astronauts. After Malenchenko returned to Earth several months later, they repeated their wedding ceremony in a Russian church. Afterwards, they went on honeymoon to Australia.

Space in space

For those who have never been inside a spacecraft – and that is basically everyone - it is rather diffi-cult to get an idea of how much space astronauts have available for working and living. Here are some enlightening numbers:

Mercury	60 cubic feet
Vostok	70.5 cubic feet
Gemini	90 cubic feet
Apollo (capsule)	924 cubic feet
Apollo (Lunar module)	235 cubic feet
Soyuz-TMA (re-entry and living compartments)	317 cubic feet
Space Shuttle (Orbiter)	2,525 cubic feet
Salyut	3,178 cubic feet
Skylab	10,594 cubic feet
Mir	13,349 cubic feet
International Space Station (as of January 1, 2005)	15,009 cubic feet
International Space Station (once assembled)	42,378 cubic feet

Cramped Conditions on board the Mir

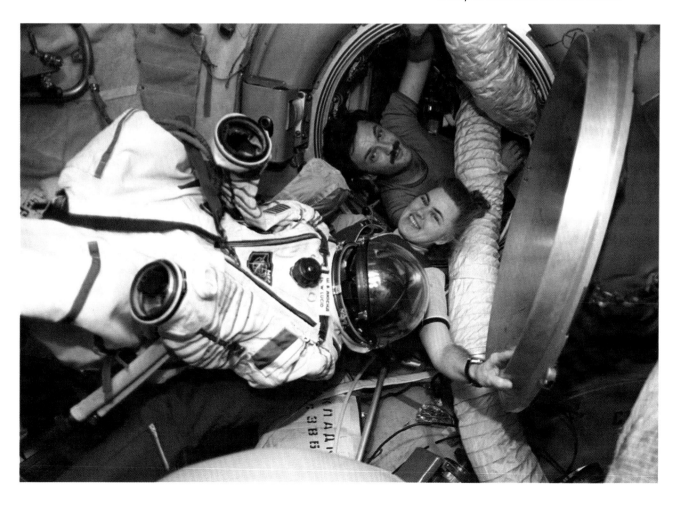

When eating in space you soon realize that you do not have enough hands. While cosmonaut Valery Korzun struggles to open a food pack, toast, a hamburger and an orange float around.

Mealtime in Mir in March 1996. Five visiting American astronauts eat, some out of a can (Russian style) and others out of plastic (American style). There is enough supply of both kinds. Containers are marked with different colors and labels. Shannon Lucid, left, stayed at the orbital station for six months.

Astronauts who neglect their exercise programs will certainly notice a change once they arrive back on Earth. It takes them much longer before they can walk and move around normally again.

A typical feature of a returning astronaut is a swollen face. It is caused by changed blood circulation. Under normal circumstances the blood pressure is higher in the feet then in the heart. The heart pumps the blood through the whole body

against gravity. In space, blood does not have the tendency to stay in the lower part of the body but it spreads all over the body instead. Within a day of arriving in space, on average one liter of water moves from the legs into the head. That process results in a swollen, red-skinned head and a feeling of having your nose permanently full. Apart from that, a considerably reduced heart activity in a state of weightlessness leads to cardiovascular muscle size reduction and a lower heartbeat rate. Also, the number of red blood cells decreases dramatically which results in various extents of anemia in astronauts. In principle, it all gets back to normal after the return to Earth. There is however, something which does not return to normal, and that is the loss of bone mass. In space, the human organism produces fewer bone cells, which means that after one month astronauts lose on average one percent of their bone mass. In the course of a several months-long mission

Fresh fruit is always welcome on any space station. Opportunity to get fresh food comes several times a year, namely when a cargo ship arrives or when visiting astronauts come on board..

American Mike Fincke juggles oranges aboard the ISS.

that percentage can nevertheless considerably increase. It is therefore no wonder that immediately upon their return, astronauts have to take it very, very easy. The body must again adapt to gravity and certain things must be unlearnt: astronauts, who spend the first night in their own bed, often feel as if they were still floating around. Many an astronaut

Who:	*Edgar Mitchell*, USA (1930)
What:	*Apollo 14*
When:	*1971*
Why:	*The sixth man on the Moon, he was secretly engaged in an experiment in extrasensory perception. After his space mission he remained interested in the subject and later founded an institute which focused on financing research on the paranormal. Mitchell remained persuaded that UFOs exist.*

inevitably comes to the realization that it is not advisable to try to put things in the air, because they just fall down on your head.

Space does not only influence the human body. The human psyche is also influenced. Being able to stay for months in a hermetically closed space with people whom you have not even chosen yourself requires substantial powers of adaptation. First of all, there is almost no privacy on board the ISS. It is not possible to go for a walk. There are cases of astronauts who did not manage to prevent arguments and consequently avoided each other for days; however, generally speaking, it usually works out surprisingly well. After all, there is a mutual goal which has to be achieved: there are experiments to be done, maintenance jobs to be carried out as well as regular 'household' duties. These mutual tasks naturally unite the crewmates. Everyone is interested in getting a positive evaluation. It is the main criterion for being in consideration for future flights. In the preparatory phase of a mission, astronauts usually do their best to get to know each other as much as possi-

Spanish astronaut Pedro Duque spent a week at the ISS in October 2003. His image is reflected in a floating drop of water.

ble. Especially in Russia, with its tradition of long-term space flights, much emphasis is laid on psychological supervision and the guidance of astronauts before, during and after their stay in space. Repeatedly, crews had to be dismissed only because the crewmates did not get along sufficiently well with one another.

Home front

Life with an astronaut can be challenging at times for family and friends. The movie 'The Right Stuff' adapted from Tom Wolfe's book of the same name depicts how the wives of the first generation of astronauts lived in the shadow of their husbands' fame. With its own interests in mind, NASA wanted to show that their heroes were living happy family lives. In consequence, the astronauts' wives had to live under the same close media scrutiny as their husbands. Early space explorers were also exposed to women who were excited by the idea of seducing an astronaut. Many a marriage was destroyed by the stress brought about by the circumstances.

Who would have a relationship with an astronaut these days knows that sacrifice is necessary for the sake of 'the thing'. Institutions and companies that must be visited in the preparatory phases of a space mission are located all over the country. Frequently those facilities are located also outside the borders, especially now that the United States and Russia have united their efforts for the sake of promoting manned space program. Those who want to go the ISS station must definitely train in both Russia and the United States. Westerners who go up in a Soyuz capsule have to spend one to two years in Star City near Moscow. Russians who fly aboard a space shuttle must temporarily settle down in Houston. Sometimes their families join them there and sometimes they stay behind. In both cases they have to find power to adapt substantially to the new circumstances.

Nowadays, astronauts' families are provided with more thorough assistance. As a rule, there is usually another astronaut at hand, often a friend of the family, who serves as a contact person. In Russia, families arrive at Baikonur several days prior to the launch and enjoy the opportunity to spend the remaining time together. Family members can watch the liftoff from a special tribune for guests. On a TV screen, they watch the very first moments inside the capsule. At Kennedy Space Center, family members as well as other guests stand on the roof of the flight control center, located adjacent to the Vehicle Assembly Building. They remain out of the reach of the media: a lesson NASA learnt back in 1986 when photographers took pictures of the parents of Christa McAuliffe as they watched their daughter die before their eyes in the immense explosion of the launch vehicle.

Even during a space flight, live contact between astronauts and their families back home is made possible by means of either television or radio. Apart from that, astronauts can always use email to communicate with their close family back on Earth. Nearly every astronaut posts a few photos of his or her family in the sleeping area. Due to the number of promotional trips and evaluative sessions, the reunion is not possible immediately after the landing. In earlier times, astronauts traveled from one town to another to tell their stories to the public. These days, they land in the midst of never-ending lectures, and formal ceremonies. Many of them feel obliged to write a book about their space experiences. Only after the PR storm calms down a bit, astronauts can return to their family lives again. However, only until he or she is nominated for another mission.

The sound of an alarm clock wakes up the crew of the ISS every morning. They unzip their sleeping bags and float out. In zero-gravity, sleeping is a special thing. It is recommended to anchor your sleeping bag properly because otherwise you might find yourself in another part of the station the next morning. Most astronauts manage to remain in a stable position during

Apollo astronaut Gene Cernan arrived at his workplace for a publicity photo.

Page 107:

Astronaut Karl Henize is about to suck in a drop of coke during a space shuttle flight in 1985. At the age of 58, Henize was one of the oldest astronauts. He was member of the space corps from 1967 and had to wait eighteen long years before he got his chance. He died in 1993 during a climb to the top of Mount Everest.

This can of beer was photographed during a joint Russian-American mission in Mir in 1997. It is widely known that alcohol has been smuggled into space.

a night's sleep but they have to fasten their sleeping bags with belts and Velcro fasteners and must not forget to put tape over their shoulders so that they do not slip out of their bags at night. Two permanent members of the station have a separate lockable cabin with a small window each. Other, usually visiting, astronauts must find their own place where it is relatively quiet and dark.

The 'bathroom' consists of a mirror fixed to the wall of one of the compartments. Everything is to be done there: washing, shaving and tooth brushing. There is no shower onboard the station: astronauts wash themselves with a wet towel. Shaving is a real challenge. If you use a razor, you have to wipe off the shaving foam quite often with a handkerchief so that it does not float around. Those who prefer to shave dry need to use a special vacuum to get rid of loose hairs. You also need this device to cut your hair. It is not desirable to have all sorts of things floating around and eventually getting into splits and

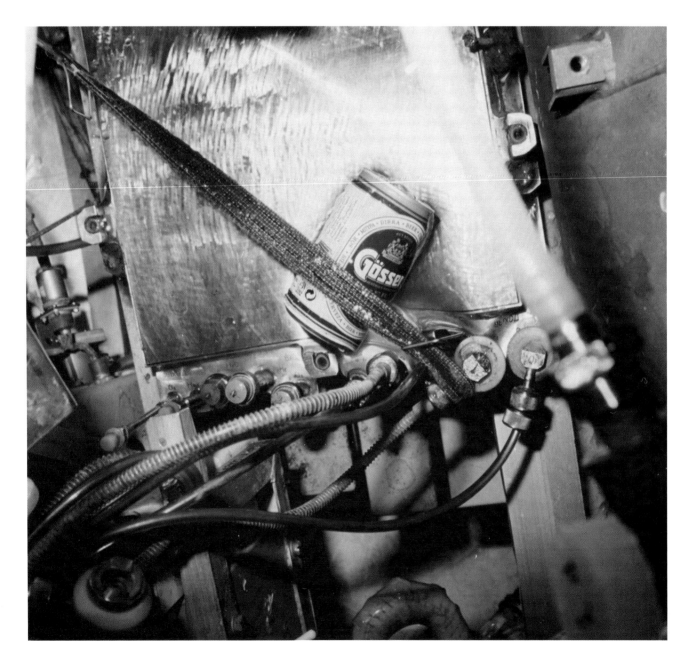

cracks in the machinery. That is also the reason why astronauts eat as little crumbling food as possible.

Eating onboard a space station used to be a rather miserable activity. The first astronauts ate mainly from tubes. The situation has improved since then. There is a small kitchenette aboard the station where you can warm your meal. There is also a collapsible eating table although strictly speaking, you do not need tables in zero-gravity. Still, it is a place which brings all the crew members together at least three times a day to eat

Astronauts Dan Bursch, Steve Smith and Tom Jones are seen here in their sleeping cabins in the space shuttle. The compartments can be closed and opened just like a closet. It is usual for astronauts to hang up their unit's or university's pennants in their sleeping place.

Cosmonaut Yuri Usachev shows off his sleeping cabin in the Mir station during a visit of Space Shuttle Atlantis crew (the Orbiter can be seen outside the window) in March 1996. Usachev made four space flights; two of them in a Soyuz and two in a shuttle.

a meal together. Plates, spoons (no knives or forks are used in space) and boxes with food can be anchored by means of a magnet and elastic tape. The menu offers a variety of food: basically everything that is available on Earth. There have even been pizza deliveries to space stations. Most food is sort of sticky so that is stays where it should and also to avoid crumbs floating around.

Astronaut Peggy Whitson floats around in the ISS station. In 2002 she spent six full months aboard the station.

Close to the eating area there is a storage room with American food in blue containers and Russian food in red ones. Most food comes dry in packs and becomes edible after adding some warm water and it can then be cut or molded. It is therefore not necessary to cook in the traditional sense of the word. Russian food usually comes in cans. Other dishes can be heated on

The ISS: Permanent residents

The station has been permanently inhabited since the end of 2000. There is always a so-called 'permanent crew' aboard which stays for months and now and then receives visitors: astronauts who stay for a shorter period of time (usually a week or two). The permanent crew's mission is referred to as an expedition. Since Expedition 7, the crew has consisted of two people because Space Shuttle Orbiters have not been available (due to the tragic accident which claimed the lives of the Columbia crew) to provide supplies and provisions to the station.

Expedition	Crew	Launch	Landing	Length
1	William Shepherd (US) Yuri Gidzenko (Rus) Sergey Krikalyev (Rus)	Oct. 31, 2000	Mar. 21, 2001	140 days
2	Yuri Usachev (Rus) Susan Helms (US) James Voss (US)	Mar. 8, 2001	Aug. 22, 2001	167 days
3	Frank Culbertson (US) Vladimir Dezhurov (Rus) Mikhail Tyurin (Rus)	Aug. 11, 2001	Dec. 17, 2001	128 days
4	Yuri Onufrienko (Rus) Dan Bursch (US) Carl Walz (US)	Dec. 5, 2001	Jun. 19, 2002	195 days
5	Valery Korzun (Rus) Sergei Treschev (Rus) Peggy Whitson (US)	Jun. 5, 2002	Dec. 7, 2002	184 days
6	Kenneth Bowersox (US) Nikolai Budarin (Rus) Donald Pettit (US)	Nov. 24, 2002	May 4, 2003	161 days
7	Yuri Malenchenko (Rus) Edward Lu (US)	Apr. 26, 2003	Oct. 28, 2003	184 days
8	Michael Foale (US) Alexander Kaleri (Rus)	Oct. 18, 2003	Apr. 30, 2004	194 days
9	Gennady Padalka (Rus) Michael Fincke (US)	Apr. 19, 2004	Oct. 24, 2004	185 days
10	Leroy Chiao (US) Salizhan Sharipov (Rus)	Oct. 14, 2004	Apr. 25, 2005	193 days
11	Sergei Krikalev (Rus) John Phillips (US)	Apr. 15, 2005	Oct. 2005	179 days
12	Valery Tokarev (Rus) Bill McArthur (US)	Oct. 2005	Mar. 2006	

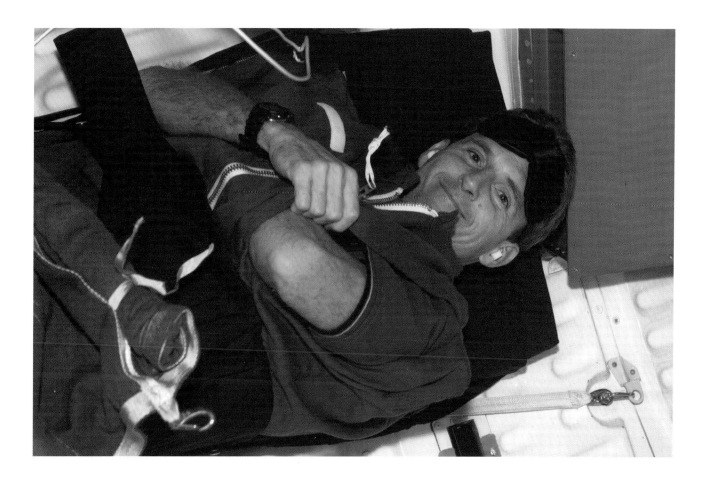

a special table equipped with heating lamps. Most astronauts notice that in zero-gravity they badly crave spicy food. 'Hot' sausages are therefore very popular. There is no fridge or deep freezer on the ISS station, at least not for private use and there is therefore no place for leftovers to be stored in. There is also no tap with cold water. Besides those regular meals, there are also snacks and fresh fruits available on board for potential visitors. Besides, astronauts themselves 'smuggle' food in their space suits. Liquor is officially forbidden in space, but it is widely known that now and then astronauts manage to smuggle some into space.

Naturally enough, there is also a toilet in the space station. Underneath the toilet seat there is a holder with a plastic bag which holds excrement. Air current sucks it in. The bag can be sealed and then stored away. Astronauts pee into a sort of vacuum hose. For female astronauts, the device has a special attachment. The sanitary situation remains rather makeshift. On Earth, Space Shuttle crews receive trainings on a model of the device and learn how to use the space toilet during their missions. The opening of the toilet seat is rather narrow, only five inches wide. Underneath it there is a camera; on a small screen the astronauts can see whether or not they are in the right position. The life of the astronauts takes place in an extremely high-tech environment but in a certain sense it is comparable to camping.

Astronauts produce other wastes. Opportunity to get rid of the waste comes several times a year, when a space shuttle or an unmanned Progress cargo ship arrives. The space shuttle can

American astronaut Jerry Linenger wakes up on the Space Shuttle Atlantis on the way to Mir in January 1997. He stayed there for four months and had rather a difficult time there: so many systems and devices failed while Linenger was at the station that mission control had serious doubts about the safety of Mir for American astronauts.

Shannon Lucid checks plants aboard the Mir orbital station, shortly before she left for Earth in docked Space Shuttle Atlantis.

Astronaut Ellen Ochoa floats next to two monitor consoles in the ISS that serve to indicate its maximum speed; 17.500 miles or 28.000 kilometers per hour – ten times the speed of a rifle bullet. The station orbits the Earth at that immense speed. However, astronauts on board the ISS can not feel it. There is no air resistance and so the space orbital station circles noiselessly around our beautiful blue planet.

take full waste bags back to Earth where they are eventually burnt in the atmosphere. Everything is done so that supplies and provisions onboard a station are used as efficiently as possible. As much water as possible is reused; there is a device onboard the ISS which serves to collect humidity from the air and transform it into usable water. That is the reason why a once used handkerchief is left out to dry: the water can be collected and reused. It is of essential importance because it takes a great deal of weight and space – and money of course – to bring new bags of water into space.

Clothing is also extremely well utilized. With the exception of liftoff and landing, when they are cramped inside inconvenient

air-tight space suits, astronauts usually wear casual clothes. They do not have much to choose from though. But let's not forget that they do not get dirty as easily as on Earth because they do not go outside. An ISS astronaut gets on average one pair of shorts and one polo shirt every three days to move around in. Work clothes are replaced every ten days. Underclothes and socks are changed every second day. Shoes are worn only on the exercise equipment. Astronauts usually wear thick woolen socks to keep their feet warm. Clothes that can not be used anymore are thrown away.

Astronauts do not have much free time, definitely not during one- or two-week missions. The free time they have for themselves is mostly spent in front of one of the station's windows with a camera in hand. Only crew members who stay over longer periods of time can afford to read a book. Each astronaut can take a limited amount of personal belongings and often there is a Discman in their baggage. Perhaps there is nothing quite so impressive as orbiting the Earth with Elton John's 'Rocketman' in your headphones. There is usually also a bag of DVDs in the station.

Every space shuttle's docking with the ISS presents a valuable opportunity to bring new supplies and provisions. Supplies brought to the station vary from fresh fruit, new DVDs and magazines to drawings from astronauts' children as well as other mail. Musical instruments, such as guitars and keyboards have also been brought to space. Much contact with home is maintained by means of email and telephone. With certain regularity, family members get a chance to come to the flight

Astronauts John Blaha and Shannon Lucid have a good time aboard Columbia in October 1993. At the time this picture was taken, Lucid was going through her 752nd hour on the space shuttle (accumulated during a number of STS missions) and at that moment she was breaking a space shuttle record.

control center and see their dear one live on screen. It is natural enough that contact with astronauts' closest relatives is made whenever possible. It is not unusual for families of astronauts to be separated for long periods. They often post a photograph or other item of personal value on the wall next to their sleeping place to make at least a small intimate nook of their own.

Those who stay over long periods of time in space soon notice that they are missing important events taking place back on Earth. Many astronauts have small kids who attend school and that comes hand in hand with all those happy moments in one's family life. Not long ago, the wife of an astronaut gave birth while her husband was in space. It was expected but everyone can image what the father must have felt. He was no different from any other loving father, he wanted to be there to see his newborn child.

Death occurs too: twice the father of an astronaut died while his son was orbiting the Earth. In the first case, it was decided not to inform the astronaut. He learnt the sad news when he came back and admitted later on that it had been the best solution. The other cosmonaut received the news while still in space. He was completely overcome by grief and could not function properly for several days. At moments like these, isolation from the rest of society is experienced with much more

Dutch astronaut Wubbo Ockels shows a picture of his daughter during a space flight in 1985.

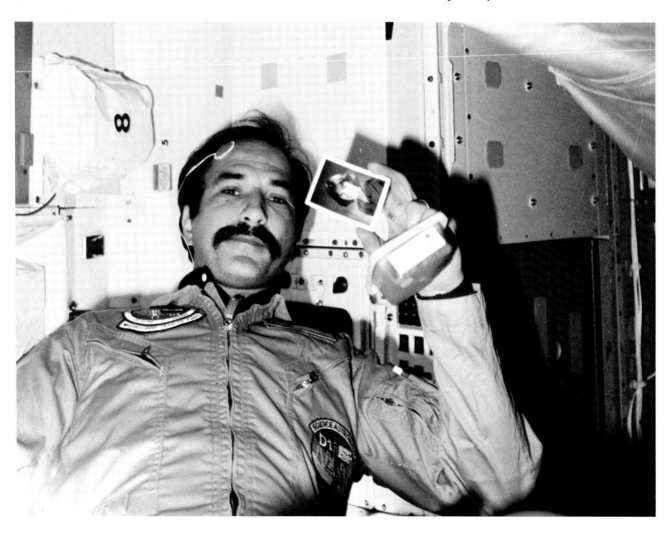

intensity. Provided that there are no interventions of this sort, astronauts try to make the best of the special situation they are in. Generally speaking, it takes a couple of days to get used to the rhythm of life in space. After a while, they are able to lean against the wall with aplomb and to float anywhere with elegance of movement. They learn to coordinate the movements of their bodies so that they can remain floating completely still on a desired spot and in a chosen position. Just like in any other unfamiliar environment it takes a while to get used to the sounds, smells and habits of the place. They learn to pay extra attention to where they leave their things because those things can be gone in no time. The once lost things often reappear again by the air-conditioning vents. You just have to know these things. You can get conditioned to life in space but it will hardly ever feel natural.

Cosmonaut Valeri Polyakov looks out of a window in the Mir space station to observe the approaching space shuttle Discovery. Polyakov spent 437 days without interruption at Mir.

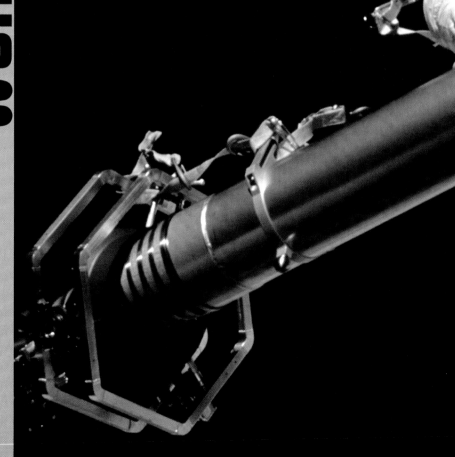

Working in Space

Working *in Space*

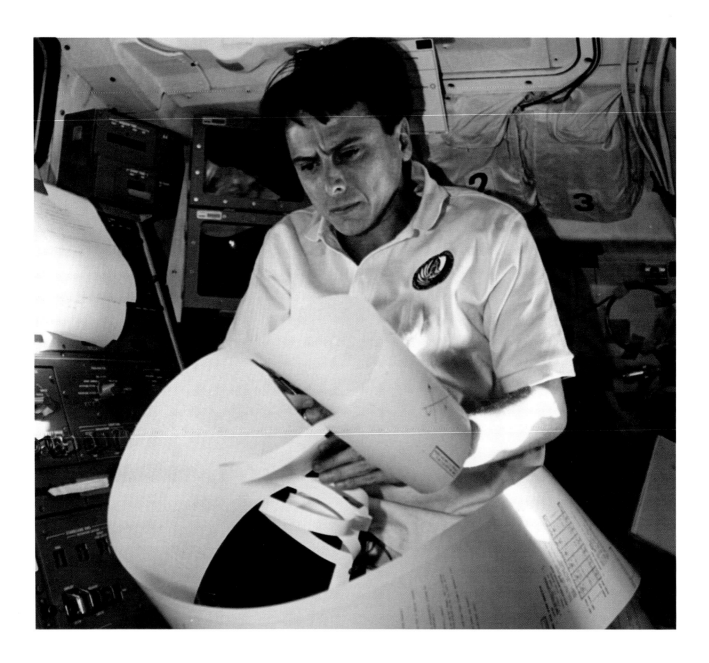

Franklin Chang-Diaz struggles with a long fax containing the instructions of the flight control in February 1994.

Page 119:
We wouldn't stick papers on the windshield of our own car, but on the space shuttle it does not cause a problem. This is astronaut Andrew Allen inside the cockpit of the Atlantis in August 1992.

It took some time before people got things up and running in space. For years, astronauts were busy checking that their spacecrafts did in fact function properly before they could focus their efforts on other things. Initially, American astronauts strongly objected to the idea of carrying out scientific experiments. They were, after all, test pilots and had hardly anything to do with science. They liked to maneuver their aircrafts and check flight controls much more than anything else. They eventually consented to take responsibility for medical tests during and after their missions. For physicians, it was of course fascinating to see the human organism functioning properly in a state of weightlessness.

We had to wait till spacecrafts and crews grew bigger and there were not only pilots aboard space vehicles but also people with specific scientific backgrounds.

In theory, it is therefore not so surprising that it took years before astronauts could focus on other things. The first space explorers delivered few scientific findings of any relevance. However, the experiments those astronauts carried out were after all vital to justifying their costly missions. Once politically attractive records were broken, a relevant question emerged: what will be the important things we are going to do up there?

Who: *Alan Shepard,* USA
(1923-1998)

Where: *On the Moon*

When: *February 1971*

Why: *Alan Shepard, the first American in space in 1961, made no secret of his ambitions to achieve more than just a small lope into orbit. He implemented some very smart tactics and put everything he had into his participation on the Moon mission. Shepard managed to become the commander of the Apollo 14 mission. He is remembered for playing golf on the Moon. Shepard brought out a couple of golf balls that he had smuggled into the module. Then he put an adapter on the end of a metal stick originally designed for an experiment and with that makeshift golf club he batted one ball after another. With the first ball he hit the Moon's ground, the second ball jumped several feet away and the third one flew away in the direction of a crater. "Miles and miles and miles", Shepard said triumphantly. He left the fourth ball behind for future Moon golfers.*

Astronaut Mae Jemison on board Spacelab in 1992; this flight received financial support from Japan. Spacelab is in the payload bay of the space shuttle. In the boxes standing against the walls is equipment for the planned experiments. Jemison was the first female African-American in space.

This issue came under serious discussion only at the end of the sixties in both the United States and the Soviet Union. To increase the scientific value of lunar missions, there was a geologist, Harrison Schmitt, put on the Apollo spacecraft

Space Shuttle Commander Charles Bolden talks to radio amateurs on earth from the cockpit of Atlantis in 1992. Bolden, a former marine, served as pilot on board two space shuttle missions and as commander of two other shuttle flights. After he finished his career at NASA he went back to the US Marine Corps.

at the very last moment. The Soviets sent a physician, Boris Yegorov, into space in a capsule.

In the beginning of the seventies, Salyut 1, the first genuine orbital module which enabled astronauts to work and live in space, was launched into orbit. The main goal of the Soviet Union at that time was to achieve the permanent presence of their cosmonauts in space. Salyut was as big as a mobile home and provided space for a permanent crew of two to three people. As a rule, they stayed there for months without interruption. At that time, the crew carried out a number of scientific experiments which were partially transported to Salyut by unmanned Progress cargo rockets.

Sick berth

Many astronauts experience problems with Space Adaptation Syndrome, a form of motion sickness, which causes nausea and overall feelings of malaise. Vomiting is the most outward symptom.
Because medical data are private, NASA has never disclosed who exactly has suffered from SAS. It is presumed that the first woman in space, Valentina Tereshkova, had a very hard time due to SAS during her flight in 1963.
The Japanese journalist who traveled to Mir, as well as both American representatives of the public who flew onboard the space shuttle went through similar bad experiences. There is medicine available in form of pills which can provide at least some relief.
Naturally enough, astronauts also suffer from other 'earthly' disorders. In October 1968, astronaut Walter Schirra suffered from a bad cold during the Apollo 7 mission while he and his two crew-mates had to test a new Apollo capsule in orbit. Both of them got infected. Years later, Shirra made a television commercial for Actifed, a cold medicine. The launching of the Apollo 9 was postponed from February 28 to March 3, 1968 when all three members started to sniffel. In February 1990, a space shuttle liftoff had to be delayed because its commander was suffering from a very bad cold.
Two people had to be evacuated from space due to disease. In September 1985 cosmonaut Vladimir Vasyutin arrived to the Salyut 7 space station. From the end of October he was no longer able to carry out his duties. He suffered from 104 degree Fahrenheit fever and had urological problems. He was given time off by the flight control center but unfortunately he did not get any better. But more than anything else, Vasyutin felt guilty for neglecting his duties. Diverse sources spoke of psychological problems and of depression. On November 13, the crew began to code their communication with the flight control so that Vasyutin's evacuation from the station could be set up and on November 21, Vasyutin was brought back to Earth. Eventually he had to spend a month in hospital to recover from what turned out to be a prostate infection.
A similar case occurred two years later. When Russian cosmonaut Alexander Laveykin came to Mir he was already in rather bad shape. During a spacewalk, mission control found out that Laveykin was suffering from cardiac arrhythmia. The cosmonaut was brought back to Earth but no abnormalities were diagnosed. Ten years later, the same defect - cardiac arrhythmia - affected cosmonaut Vasili Tsibliyev, the commander of the Mir orbital station just as he had to face the infamous fire, the collision with Progress as well as other problems onboard the station. Nevertheless, he managed to finish his round of duties.

Experiments provided data in various fields of science: material physics, biology, medicine, physiology. The equipment was usually stored in special boxes that were later fixed to the inner walls of the station. From the beginning of the seventies, the Soviets gradually launched seven manned Salyut modules into orbit. In 1986, the Salyut type of orbital station was replaced by the bigger and more famous Mir.

As a rule, a space station crew received a mission plan from their flight control center. That plan contained detailed descriptions of activities that were to be carried out. The astronauts' activities varied from the simple switching on and off of otherwise fully automatic experiments to detailed descriptions of plant growth, operating of a melt-

German astronaut Hans Schlegel does a headstand without touching the ground in the Spacelab in 1993. In the background, his colleague Bernard Harris is busy working on an experiment. The lab was financed by the German government, which enabled Schlegel and his countryman Ulrich Walter to participate in the mission.

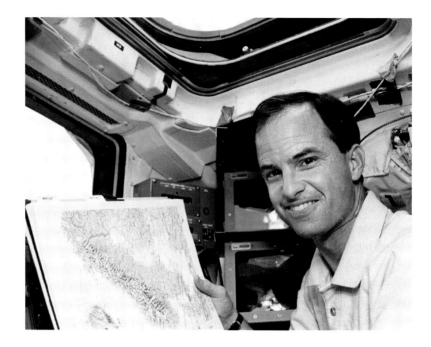

Astronaut Kevin Chilton consults an atlas on board the Space Shuttle Endeavor in April 1994. The atlas was used to find objects for a radar device in the payload bay. The locations that were chosen were consequently scanned both by the radar and by a camera from the cockpit.

American astronaut Charles Precourt floats in the Kristall module of Mir in the summer of 1995.

ing furnace or carrying out medical research on crewmates. In principle, all these experiments were prepared beforehand. Astronauts had to be able to fulfill the role of laboratory assistants. If needed, they could get further instructions from the researchers on Earth. It is a considered unfortunate that very few of those laboratory experiments were

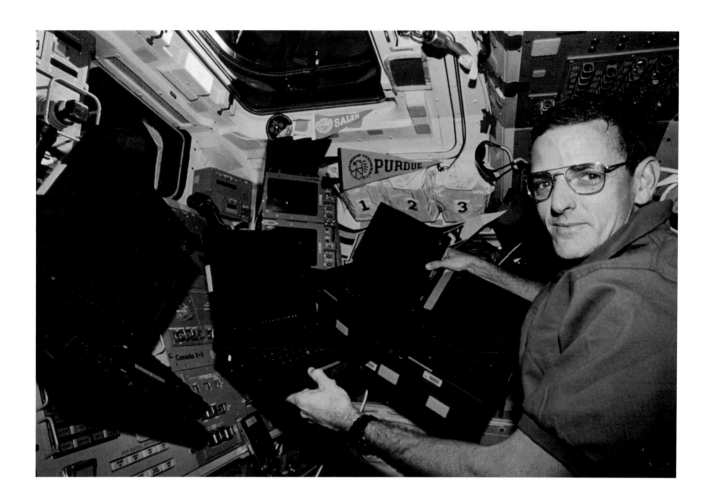

later described in Western scientific publications. In fact, the numerous experiments never delivered any astonishing new data.

Another, no less important part of the astronauts' work onboard, consisted of doing odd jobs in the station. The older an orbital station grew, the more problems occurred.

Astronaut William McArthur juggles four laptops. Laptops are essential for work in space and each astronaut has his own. They are also much faster and more powerful than the rather outdated computers on space shuttles.

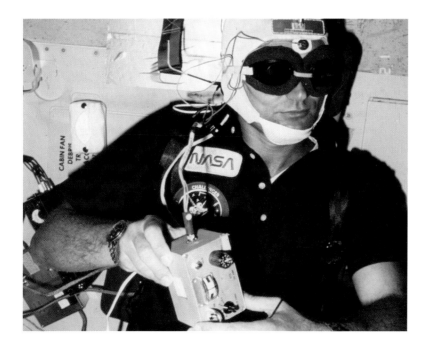

Astronaut Norman Thagard participates on a medical experiment during a space shuttle flight in 1983.

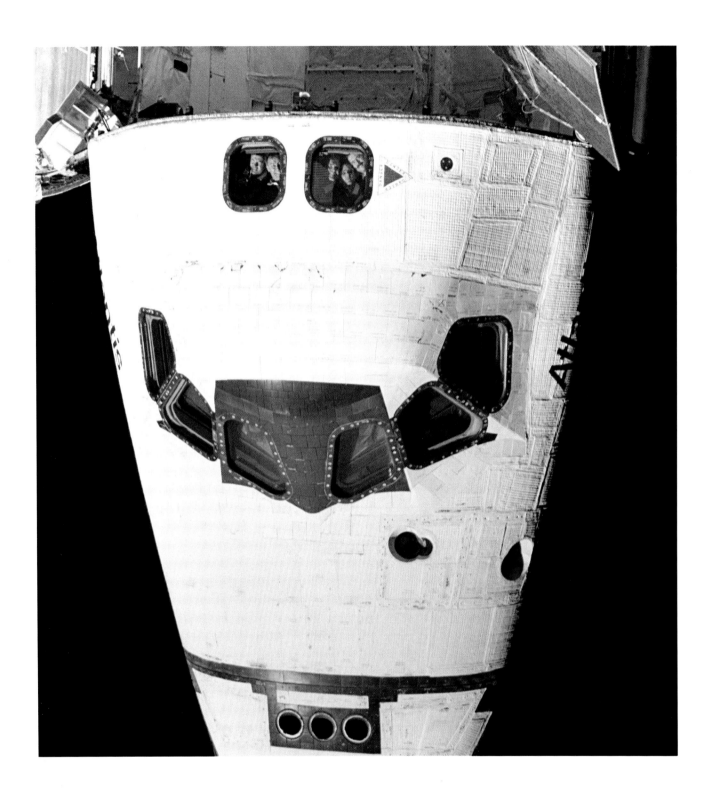

Five crew members of the Space Shuttle Atlantis look out of the window at their colleague who is taking photos from the Mir orbital station which they left shortly before. In the front fuselage of Atlantis, you can see outlets of thrusters which enable the space shuttle to maneuver in the Earth's orbit.

Especially the last years of Mir's existence were dramatic. Failings were exaggerated because at that time there were also Westerners on board and they brought along unusual media attention. There were periods during which a crew could hardly focus on science because they had to deal with one defective piece of equipment after another: the carbon dioxide filter, oxygen equipment, main computer. The year 1997 was especially disastrous in this aspect. A Progress cargo ship collided with one of the station's modules and inflicted heavy damage. At another time, a cosmonaut accidentally unplugged the wrong cable

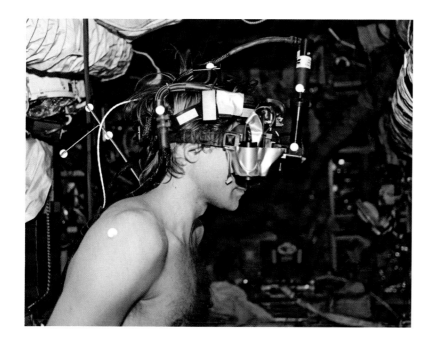

Cosmonaut Sergey Avdeyev undergoes an experiment in 1995 which tested his sense of balance.

The STS 90 Space Shuttle mission astronauts are nearly unrecognizable in the tangle of wires during a neurological examination. Astronauts as well as numerous animals (rats, mice, snails and fish among them) were subjected to neurological tests during this Neurolab mission. It was the sixteenth and last mission during which the European-made Spacelab was used to accommodate scientific equipment. To gain extra space, Spacelab was placed in the large payload bay of the space shuttle.

which resulted in a loss of balance. There was even a fire on board Mir.

Routine maintenance operations need to be carried out from outside the station as well. Doing odd jobs is much more difficult and demanding in space than on Earth. A lack of air is the first stumbling block on the list. Astronauts get

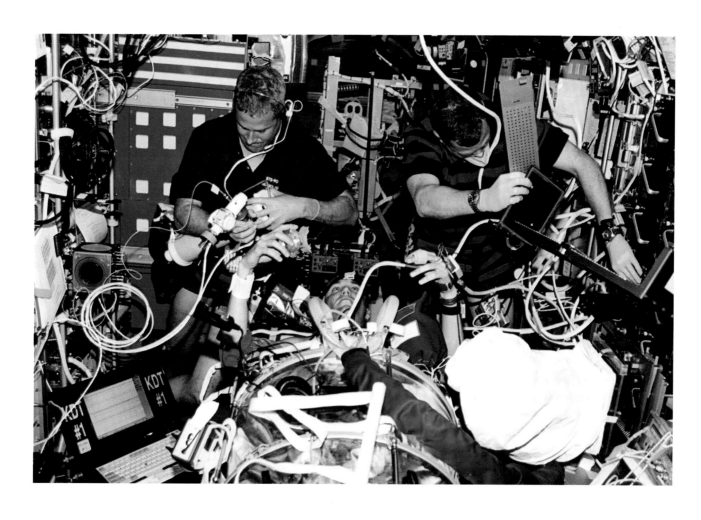

into a special air-tight space suit which in principle functions the same way as a deep sea diving suit. They enter space through an air lock. A spacewalker is connected to the station by means of a cable so that he can not float away into deep space. A rescue operation would be virtually

Records

Astronaut to spend the longest time in space: Sergei Krikalev (Russia): over 748 days over six space-flights; he is the first to serve two stints aboard the ISS.

The longest space flight: Valeri Polyakov (Russia) arrived on the Mir orbital station on January 8, 1994 and returned to earth after 437 days there.

The most experienced spacewalker: Anatoly Solovyev (Russia): 77 hours and 41 minutes over sixteen spacewalks.

The most space flights: Franklin Chang-Diaz and Jerry Ross (USA) both made seven flights in space shuttles. In total, Chang-Diaz spent 62 days and Ross 58 days in space.

The fastest astronaut: during a descent to earth the Apollo 10 capsule reached the speed of 11 107 meters (7 miles) per second.

The furthest distance from Earth: during their flight to the Moon in April 1970, the Apollo 13 astronauts found themselves 267,370.67 miles from Earth.

The most patient astronaut: Leonid Kadenyuk (Ukraine) was admitted into the Soviet space corps in 1976. In 1997, 21 years and 3 months later, he finally made his first space flight on a space shuttle. He spent two weeks there. He left active service one year later. American Don Lind was admitted into NASA space corps in 1966 and had to wait till 1985 before his day finally came. He spent a week on the space shuttle and one year later he left NASA.

The youngest astronaut: Gherman Titov (Russia) was 25 when he became the world's second astronaut in 1961.

The oldest astronaut: John Glenn (United States) was 77 when he made his second flight into space in 1998. His first flight took place in 1962. Other astronauts older than sixty years who flew into space are: Michael Melvill (he was 64 when he flew on a privately operated spacecraft SpaceShipOne in 2004), Story Musgrave (flew at the age of 61 in the space shuttle in 1996) and Dennis Tito (a space tourist, was 60 when he went into orbit in 2001).

Astronaut with the least complex training: Valentina Tereshkova, daughter of a tractor driver and a textile factory worker, was eight when she went to school for the first time. Another eight years later she left school to work in a textile factory. Apart from that, she followed some correspondence courses. In her free time she liked to go parachute jumping. Valentina was 26 when she went into space as the first woman in 1963.

Astronaut Jerry Ross shows flight insignias of the seven space shuttle missions he made in the course of his career. The picture was taken onboard the ISS station in April 2002..

impossible in such a case. Astronauts carry their air supply in a backpack, as well as the necessary electronic devices which control cooling and communication. Several times, a space 'scooter' has been tested, a gigantic backpack which allows maneuvering by means of small rockets attached to the suit. In those cases, the astronaut did not need to be anchored to the station. Those experiments provided us with some spectacular pictures of astronauts as human

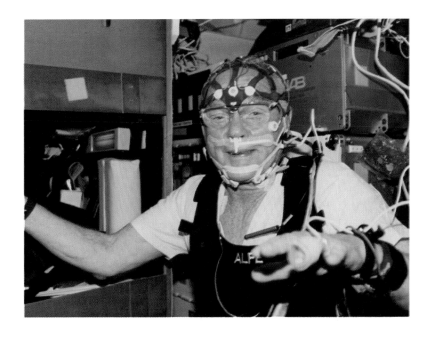

During his second space mission in 1998, the former Senator John Glenn was more than anything else a guinea pig for medical research. Since he was very curious to know how his aging organism would react to a state of zero-gravity he himself requested testing. In this picture, Glenn gets ready for an experiment which would scan his sleep phases. There was a lot of criticism coming from scientific circles which doubted the true value of the experiments. One person's results can hardly deliver data applicable to larger groups of people.

satellites, photographed floating free against a pitch black sky.

Actual spacewalking is an exhausting activity. The space suit is definitely not the most practical outfit to move around in – especially when you float and lack any firm grip. In weightlessness, it is difficult to do even the simplest of jobs: tighten a screw for example. Zero-gravity makes it very difficult to prevent your body from turning in the same direction as the screwdriver. Special tools have therefore been designed for such minor jobs in open space. They have been thoroughly tested on Earth in an enormous swimming pool in the training center. When they return to the safety of their spacecraft, astronauts usually float dead on their feet.

In NASA jargon, spacewalking is called Extravehicular Activity (EVA). Walks on the moon were thus also classified as EVAs, even though they did not take place in zero-gravity

Cosmonaut Sergey Avdeyev in Mir during a 'revealing' experiment in 1995. Adhesive tapes were put on his body which was then scanned by an infrared camera. The experiment provided a picture of body movements in zero-gravity. No other man was as experienced in zero-gravity as Sergey Avdeyev. In total, he spent 747 days in space, in the course of his three flights.

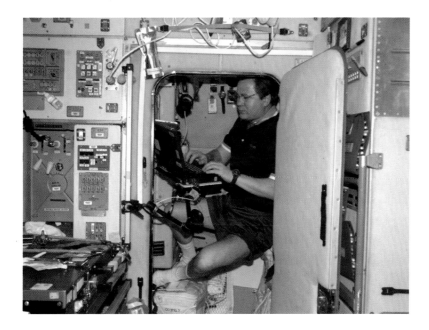

Cosmonaut Nikolai Budarin is working on a laptop in his personal cabin aboard the ISS station.

but in one-sixth of Earth's gravity. An awful lot depended on the astronauts during the landing on the moon. The last part of the descent was carried out manually, which turned out to be best. Without the intervention of Neil Armstrong,

Astronaut Carl Walz in the company of a number of jerrycans filled with water on the ISS. The plastic cans are transported there and back on both the space shuttle and the Russian Progress cargo rocket.

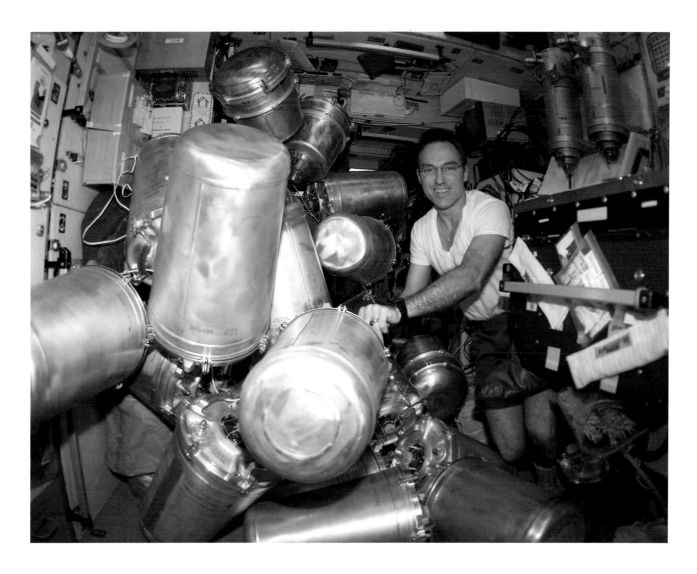

the Eagle, the lunar landing module of the Apollo 11 mission would have ended up in a field full of rocks. Thanks to their prior basic geological training, the astronauts were able to pick up some interesting stones. Apollo missions delivered TV images which we enjoy watching even today.

Who: *Valery Ryumin, Russia (1939)*

What: *Salyut 6, Mir*

When: *From 1977*

Why: *"I felt like crawling across the table and cracking his head", an American astronaut allegedly said about Valery Ryumin, who went into space for the first time in 1977 and consequently made two more Soyuz missions, became flight commander in Moscow in 1981 and from 1992 held the post of chairman of the Russian Agency for Cooperation between the US and Russia in the Mir program. 'What a nursery up there,' Ryumin is claimed to have said in 1997 when cosmonauts on the Mir had to struggle with one technical hitch after another. In his view, American astronauts were inferior to Russian cosmonauts; he openly despised astronauts with little experience and as far as he was concerned women should never have been sent into space – even though his own wife was a cosmonaut. Ryumin will be remembered as an authoritarian grouch who reserved a place for himself on the space shuttle in 1998 in order to carry out an inspection of, at that time, an already rather shaky Mir.*

Through the numerous live radio and television programs, the public had the opportunity to become familiar with the exceptional language of astronauts and flight controllers. The 'NASA-speak' was the most efficient form of communication astronauts had in their high-tech environment

Cosmonaut Sergey Zalyotin checks plants in a rather modest conservatory in the ISS.

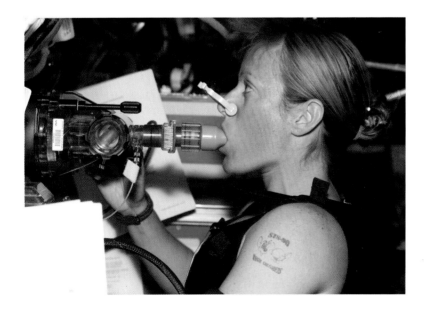

Astronaut Kathryn Hire carries out a lung function test aboard Space Shuttle Columbia in April 1998, a flight which was committed to medical research. On her upper arm she is wearing – undoubtably a removable – tattoo of the mission insignia.

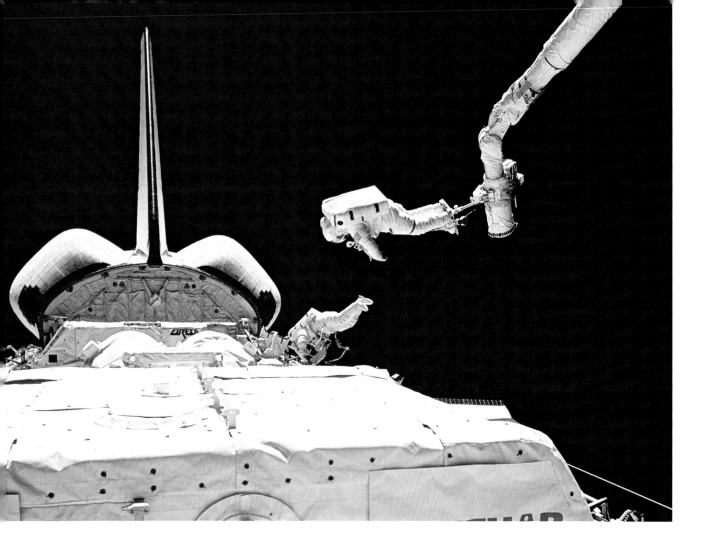

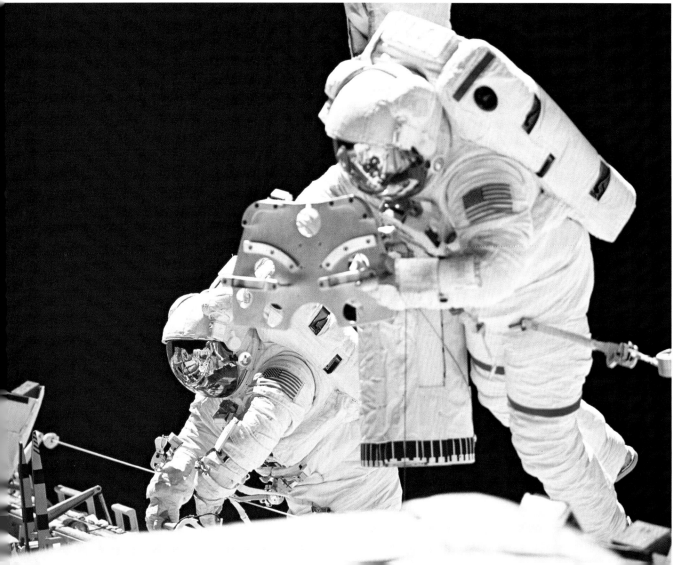

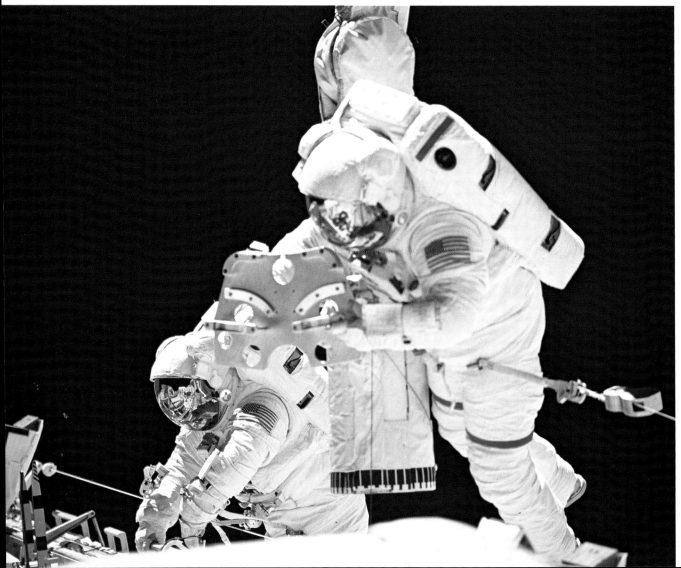

packed as it was with a myriad of switches and controls. Without further explanation, their language was hardly comprehensible to the public ear, which further increased the atmosphere of mystery which prevailed around the astronauts in the media and with the public. The astronauts found themselves in an extraterrestrial environment speaking extraterrestrial vocabulary.

Everybody who watched the television programs remembers how they felt and where they were when the first people landed on the moon. Nowadays, people live in space stations and strive for the most routine way of space exploration because it is at the same time the most cost efficient

On this and previous page: June 1993, Jeff Wisoff and David Low perform a spacewalk in the payload bay of Space Shuttle Endeavor. They are out to repair a nonfunctional antenna on the European instrumental platform.

Astronaut Jerry Ross looks through the windows of Space Shuttle Atlantis during a spacewalk in April 1991. In the course of this walk a broken antenna of the Gamma Ray observatory (in the foreground) had to be folded manually. The satellite was later put into orbit from the payload bay of Shuttle.

Page 139:
Sherwood Spring holds a four-storey tall structure during a spacewalk in December 1985. Spring stands at the end of a robotic articulating arm of the shuttle.

and risk free way. Of course, there are still moments of excitement but the vast majority of time in a space station is taken up with everyday routine and troubleshooting. Problem solving represents an important part of the day-to-day tasks. That may sound exciting, but in fact it includes, for example, the repairing of a defective toilet. Because

Astronomic salaries

Astronauts have nice jobs but they do not get paid astronomic salaries. A pilot of a civilian aircraft earns much more. American astronauts in the first group at the end of the fifties were offered between 8,330 and 12,770 American dollars depending on their age and experience. The income of NASA astronauts is nowadays based on governmental salary scales 11 to 13 which pay between 56,257 and 86,974 USD per year. There are also perks and bonuses which can increase the final sum. European astronauts are better off. They earn between 84,000 and 96,000 euros, after tax. The first three European astronauts, selected in 1978, were paid even more than that. When an ESA astronaut flies into space his or her salary goes up. Yang Liwei, the first Chinese in space, earns 10.000 Yuan (1200 USD) a month. Russian cosmonauts are at the bottom of the list, they must put up with a few hundred dollars a month unless they are trained for a space shuttle mission in the United States where they receive American salaries.
Cosmonauts are subjected to a system of merit bonuses. During a space mission they receive extra daily allowances that can be collected after their return to earth. They can increase their salary in the course of their mission through the proper execution of various tasks. Spacewalks are rewarded with a special bonus just as manually operated coupling of modules. In the case of accidents, they can forget about extras. Undesired incidents can even result in salary cuts. In 1975, two cosmonauts had to make a doubtful emergency landing some twenty minutes after the liftoff. They landed in an inhospitable area, made a few somersaults in the capsule and ended up in a mountain slope. They could forget about the 3,000 ruble bonus. The money was eventually paid out but only after the crew protested to the party leader Brezhnev.

Astronaut Robert Stewart floats freely above Earth in February 1984, several dozen feet from Space Shuttle Challenger. Stewart is sitting in a so-called 'Manned Maneuvering Unit', a kind of rocket-operated seat. By means of controls and switches on the armrests, he can operate small propelling rockets and maneuver in space. This was the first time a spacewalk was conducted without the astronaut being anchored with a cable to the spacecraft.

everything floats in space, toilet contents not excluded, the job is even more undesirable in zero-gravity than on Earth. The last crew of Mir could tell you stories about it. It is sometimes exceptionally frustrating not to be able to get a defective device back to work even despite months of technical maintenance training back on Earth. Prior to their expeditions, the permanent crew learnt how to fulfill the roles of electricians and mechanics in space. They have to be aware of how all the technical systems on board work. From earlier crews, they learnt that improvisation is an important element in keeping the environment inhabitable at the station. The strategy is outlined by the flight control people on Earth, but the actual job has to be done by the astronauts themselves.

Astronauts Rick Hieb (outside) and Tom Akers (inside) are posing by the back window in the cockpit of Space Shuttle Endeavor. The big joystick in the middle of the controls panel enables the operation of the shuttle's robotic arm (Remote Manipulator System in NASA jargon) which serves to move big objects into and out of the payload bay.

Page 140:
Space Shuttle Columbia mission organized for the purpose of repairing the Hubble Telescope in February 2002. Above the payload bay you can see two servicemen floating; the telescope can be seen at the back.

Russians have so far gained thirty years experience operating a manned space station. It seemed quite uncertain at first but no one will doubt that keeping a space station in operation for such a long time is a great achievement – even despite financial and technical setbacks. With their Moon landings, Americans followed a completely different course. They concentrated on the development of a space transport system that has in every aspect evolved into

Astronaut Rex Walheim waves to the camera during a spacewalk outside the ISS in April 2002.

Three astronauts take hold of a communication satellite during a spacewalk in May 1992. The satellite was brought into the wrong orbit level by an unmanned rocket and astronauts were requested to 'catch' it so that it could be flown at the correct level.

Page 145:
This picture reveals astronaut Mike Lopez-Alegria during a spacewalk in October 2000. In his helmet you can see a reflected image of Space Shuttle Discovery (with its Remote Manipulator System) and the ISS.

a multifunctional vehicle. The shuttle can function as a ferry to space stations, as service for defective satellites, as a laboratory and as a point of departure for artificial satellites that were sent on their way from there.

Over the course of the years, the shuttle has been used for all these tasks. The space station came much later than originally expected. The shuttle had been a goal on its own for some twenty years. In the first years, many satellites were brought up in the payload bay that were then put out in the orbit or were launched into higher orbits by means of small rocket engines. Some satellites were also repaired in space. The Spacelab was repeatedly taken into payload bay which enabled scientific experiments to be carried out. After the crash of the Challenger, no more commercial satellites were launched from the shuttle vehicles. Since the end of nineties, virtually every mission has served the assembly

of the ISS. The intention is that all scientific research will be moved there because the facilities are better and enable longer experiments to take place without disruptions. For years, the shuttle will be serving as a floating cargo ship for construction materials – and construction workers.

Work in the shuttle differs considerably from work in a space station. Time in a space shuttle is quite limited (a mission takes one to two weeks only) and that makes it very costly. Almost every single minute is described in the mission timetable. Every day, the crew receives an updated version. It says which experiments should be carried out at which time, how long a lunch break should take, how much time spacewalks can take etc. Many activities are rehearsed

Who:	*Georgi Ivanov*, *Bulgaria* (*1940*)
What:	*Soyuz 33*
When:	*1978*

Why: *Originally he was supposed to spend a week in space, but he returned after only two days. Ivanov was a guest of the Soyuz 33 capsule which flew to the Salyut space station. Nikolai Rukavishnikov held the function of flight commander. The docking of the module with the station went wrong due to a technical failure. The cosmonauts had to return to earth at once. The return journey did not go smoothly either: due to a miscalculation, gravity was much stronger than was thought, and the capsule landed 100 miles from the calculated location of touchdown. The space adventure of the Bulgarian cosmonaut was over after 31 orbits around Earth. Nevertheless, at home he was received as a national hero and received countless accolades. Years later he was considered for another space mission.*

on Earth to find out how much time is needed for them. In the case of scientific missions, more activities are done simultaneously so that less time is wasted. Often, astronauts must work overtime. There are therefore hardly any really spontaneous moments aboard the shuttle; there is always something to be done.

Astronauts and cosmonauts who make a short mission to the ISS in a Soyuz capsule are also subjected to similar hec-

Astronauts Tom Akers and Kathy Thornton practice assembling a platform in space during a space shuttle flight in 1992.

This is what I call a workplace with a view. Astronauts Story Musgrave and Jeffrey Hoffman do routine maintenance on the Hubble Telescope in December 1993. They have fastened themselves to the gigantic robotic arm of the Space Shuttle Endeavor. In the background you can see the west coast of the Australian continent. Once the telescope was repaired it was put back into space where it continued to function for many years.

Kathy Thompson inspects her equipment during a spacewalk in December 1993 when she repaired the Hubble Telescope.

tic schemes. Many of the missions last only a week or so and during that time the (often paying) guests have to do as much work as possible. High sums of money are always paid to get them there and the efficiency must therefore be extremely high. Astronauts who already live at the station have a different perception of time since they stay for months in the station. Their working week in space does not actually differ so greatly from that on Earth; the majority of their weekends is free. Nevertheless, you will hardly be able to forget about your job when you live at the place of your employment.

Nearly every recent space shuttle flight has brought new modules and equipment to space. And so, the station has gradually grown from one cylinder-shaped module to a whole maze of compartments and solar panels. The activities required to keep the whole thing going are quite demanding on the permanent crew. One of the reasons is that in place of the originally planned crew of six, there are only two due to cost-cutting measures. In principle, there is an American and a Russian astronaut stationed permanently. That is the absolute minimum and it limits the possibility of carrying out scientific experiments. The expecta-

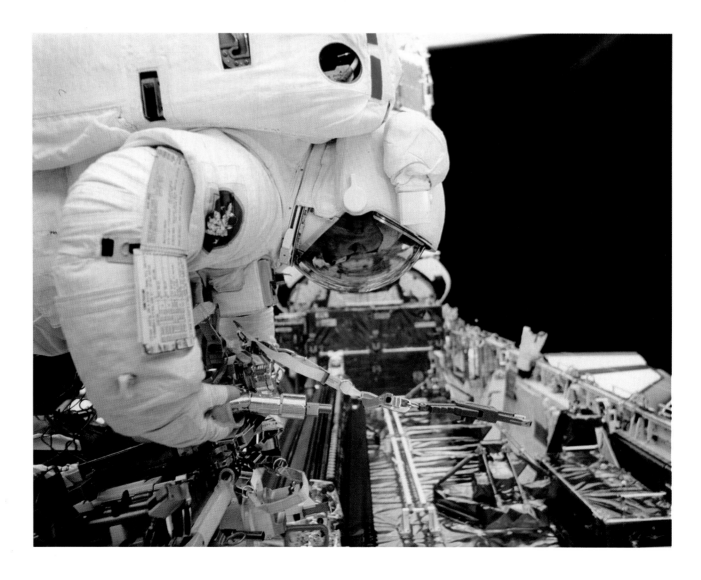

tions of the ISS as a scientific space lab were much greater in the beginning. If you believed the space agencies' statements, Nobel prizes should have been raining on astronauts. Cancer, Aids, osteoporosis: the space station was expected to deliver considerably to medical research on numerous earthly diseases. The reality turned out to be less optimistic. The quantity – and consequently also the

VIPs in space

The time will come when tourists fly into space on a more or less regular basis. Till that time paying space travelers will have to put up with chairs offered by Russians in their Soyuz capsules. It has happened twice so far: American Dennis Tito and South African Mark Shuttleworth who were ready and willing to splurge on it – twenty million dollars in cash. They had to go through months of training at Star City and they both spent a week in space.

Naturally enough, there are wealthy people ready to pay. The first was the American country music singer John Denver. He let NASA know that he would like to go into space on a space shuttle. Denver underwent a medical examination in Johnson Space Center and was given a thorough excursion throughout the complex. But he had to abandon his plans when the Space Shuttle Challenger exploded. From that moment on there has been no place for civilian astronauts. At the end of the eighties the Russians were asking ten million dollars a seat (now the price is twice as high) and that turned out to be too much, even for the well-heeled Denver. Above all, Denver did not fancy the idea of having to spend months training in Russia.

Young people will know Lance Bass, the singer who is a member of the music band N'Sync. In autumn 2002, it seemed that he would get on a Soyuz capsule. He was of twenty-three at that time so he would have become the world's youngest astronaut. Bass turned up at Star City in springtime of that year and posed for photographers in a space suit. He took part in training sessions with his two colleagues and even set up a press conference. He was also expected to pay twenty million dollars. He planned to put that money together with the help of sponsors and by producing a seven-part documentary series. However, two months before the planned departure, the Russians realized that he had not yet paid a single cent. As result, Bass was kicked out of the mission.

And there have been other celebrities with space aspirations. James Cameron, director of the cash cow 'Titanic' is one of them. He does not want to be just an idle tourist, he wants to get to make a movie about his space experiences. However, nothing has been heard of the project lately. Russian actor Vladimir Steklov had to drop out at the last moment in 2000 when the production company which planned to make a film of his space journey did not manage to put together enough money. Steklov had been training for six months to be able to fly to Mir. But "The Last Journey" as was the intended name of the movie never came about. Steklov was kicked out a month before the scheduled departure. The two remaining cosmonauts turned out to be the last two visitors to Mir.

This picture reveals a space pas de deux (leg show for two) of astronauts Carl Meade and Mark Lee in September 1994. They are testing a new maneuver system which was designed to bring an astronaut into safety in case he unexpectedly disconnects from the cable which anchors him to the space shuttle.

quality – of experiments has always been substantially limited by the space available (it will take a long time before all parts of the ISS are in place; some modules have even been taken off the program), by limited logistics

Lance Bass, when there were reasons to be overjoyed

Astronaut Mark Lee floats in space free as a bird. On his back there is a device which allows him to maneuver so that he can return to the space shuttle on his own.

(transport has relied solely on Russian rockets since the Columbia accident) and by limited personnel available to carry out the experiments.

Certainly whenever astronauts are asked to risk their lives, there must be a sound reason. Scientific progress is one of the most important reasons for the station's existence. Nevertheless, not all scientists are ardent supporters of experiments on manned space stations. For medical or physiological purposes, there are simply not enough test subjects to provide an accurate and adequate amount of data. Purporting scientific research as the main reason behind manned space exploration is far from the truth. But doing no research at all when the opportunity exists would be a shameful waste; the station is there after all.

It is nevertheless certain that keeping the ISS in orbit, a task to which many nations contribute, serves an important political goal. An industrialized nation which is serious about its standing in the world, feels obliged to participate in the ISS program. We may doubt the motives, but the ISS is real and it is there. Such great former rivals as Russia and

Astronaut Dan Barry has a good time during his spacewalk in January 1996. He tested miscellaneous pieces of equipment used for assembling the ISS.

the United States can prove on the ISS project that they are capable of mutual cooperation. In space, countries can put their abilities on display and the costs that inevitably come along are seen by governments as worth it. However, it is still impossible to speak of an objective manner for measuring the efficiency and usefulness of space exploration. Space exploration itself is not that difficult – provided that everything works as it should.

Paranormal astronauts

Astronauts are smart and capable people whose opinion is not easily undermined. There are astronauts who have confessed to having seen unidentified flying objects. We have reason to believe there could be a conspiracy. But why do we never hear anything on this subject from the authorities?

There are numerous rumors that can be put to rest by the experts. There was for example a habit of putting full trash bags out of spacecrafts. People who then heard astronauts speak of 'four artificial objects in the vicinity of the spacecraft', as was the case with American astronaut Lowell and Aldrin in 1966, could easily jump to the wrong conclusion.

Several times, astronauts poked fun at those who eagerly questioned them about the supernatural. Delight in the UFO community was immense when cosmonaut Georgi Grechko revealed at the end of the seventies that during his fitness training he saw 'mysterious objects' out the window of the Salyut 6 space station. Years later, Grechko admitted that it was just a joke. In reality, what he saw were only loose fragments of the external coating of the station which fell off due to vibrations he caused by his movements.

It would certainly be simplistic to stereotype astronauts as complete skeptics. Quite the contrary, they seem to be quite diversified in this aspect. One of the first cosmonauts, Pavel Popovich became chairman of an umbrella organization of Russian UFO enthusiasts.

The most famous example of an astronaut who took an interest in the paranormal is Edgar Mitchell, pilot of the Apollo 14 mission. Nobody ever questioned him on the scientific experiments which he conducted on the Moon's surface but he is constantly asked to tell of the extrasensory observations that he attempted to carry out off the record and out of sight of his colleagues on the way to the moon and back. Scientists and journalists who contradicted him upon having analyzed the data have according to Mitchell, "'no sense of statistics". After he left NASA Mitchell got substantially more involved in studies of the paranormal. He founded a New Age institute which studies human consciousness.

And then there is Gordon Cooper, a late Mercury mission astronaut. Gordon became a devoted supporter of belief in the existence of UFOs. In 2000 he published his autobiography 'Leap of Faith' in which a whole chapter is dedicated to this issue. In the text he fiercely criticizes the politics of the American government. He claims that his "good and trustworthy friends and colleagues" saw unexplained things which they did not dare to report to their superiors. Since the nineteen forties, Cooper says, the governments have been trying to keep information on UFOs from the public. As jet fighter pilot and astronaut he did not dare to speak on that topic until he retired. A believer in UFOs could hardly think of a more reliable witness. Or is it only more proof that astronauts are also only human?

The space station orbits the Earth on its own momentum, though now and then you have to use some fuel to get it into a higher orbit. Astronauts fulfill a role similar to that of people paid to survey the entrance of a posh hotel; they check the controls and when something goes wrong they receive a warning signal.

Only then the crew can prove that they have gone through sufficient emergency procedure trainings and that they are capable of improvisation in unexpected situations. During the Apollo 13 mission to the Moon, these abilities saved the mission as well as astronauts' lives. The adventures of the

Astronaut Leroy Chiao gives a thumbs up during a spacewalk in January 1996 which was carried out from Space Shuttle Endeavor.

A spacewalker peeps in through a roof window of Space Shuttle Atlantis. Astronauts Marsha Ivins, Ken Cockrell and Mark Polanski are working inside the spacecraft.

Page 157:
German astronaut Thomas Reiter and Russian cosmonaut Sergey Avdeyev carry out a spacewalk during a Euro Mir 95 flight which originated from cooperation between the European Space Agency and the Russians.

Astronaut Jim Voss during a spacewalk in September 1995 in the course of which he was scheduled to test equipment for the ISS. He is fastened with his feet to a small platform.

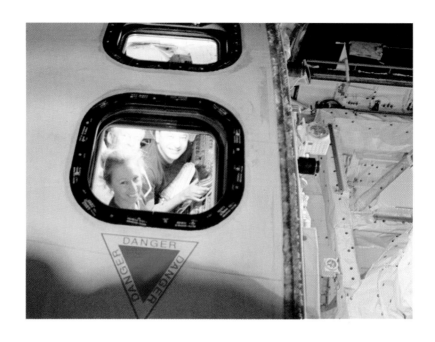

team were dramatic enough to provide sufficient material for a successful movie. Similar moments took place also onboard Mir station in 1997. A Russian and an Afghan cosmonaut got into a life-threatening situation when the

engine of their Soyuz capsule which was taking them back to Earth failed. At such moments, it is all up to the crew's sangfroid and presence of mind. Such situations show that not anyone can become an astronaut.

Many people hope that space will eventually become accessible to the masses. Tourists will fly into space only for the fun of it, not for the hardships. In 2004, the first privately

Commercials in Space

Initially NASA did not consider it a very suitable idea to equip John Glenn with a camera during the first American orbital flight around earth. That would have only diverted the astronaut's attention from other tasks. Nevertheless, eventually they were persuaded. They started working on a special camera design because that is how it is with space missions: in principle, everything that goes up must be designed especially for the given mission. But John Glenn did not feel like waiting. Shortly before his flight he purchased a simple Minolta camera in a supermarket which he then took along. And for Minolta it was a dream: free publicity.

Since then, companies have become much more attuned to the commercial opportunities of manned space flights. In 1965, after a number of tests, NASA decided that its astronauts would be wearing Omega wristwatches. Since 1968, the Fisher Space Pen has been in use in space. It is a pen equipped with a special ink cartridge which automatically displaces ink, even in zero-gravity. In 1985, both Pepsi and Coca Cola made an attempt to serve their drinks during space missions from special taps and drinking bottles. The experiment itself was a failure but attracted great publicity. As far as food is concerned, M&M has a permanent place in space under its own trademark. Generally speaking, NASA is hesitant about commercial interests in its spacecrafts. NASA is after all financed by the government and those financial resources should not be used for promoting commercial enterprises.

That has led to some strange episodes. Since the beginning of the nineties, the former rival for whom the very word 'commercial' had meant the devil himself, set on a completely different course. To fill the Russian treasury, people were taken into space for millions of dollars but money was made on a smaller scale too. All of a sudden, big boards went up all over flight control centers, commercials were heard from loudspeakers on the launch bases and there were guest cosmonauts with company logos on their space suits. In 1997, when so much was going wrong with the Mir station, cosmonauts had to reserve time for making a joyful television commercial spot for Israeli milk. Tnuva, the Israeli company, is said to have paid 450,000 dollars for a thirty-second spot. Pizza Hut had a commercial made in which its pizza is delivered to the Mir station and for one million dollars, the company bought advertisement space on a part of a rocket which transported a part of the ISS into orbit.

Cosmonauts in the Mir, and nowadays in the Russian module of the ISS, are much more often employed for advertising. Pepsi paid five million dollars for a commercial which was filmed during a spacewalk around a big Pepsi can brought there by a cosmonaut. The electronics company Radio Shack provided cosmonaut Yuri Usachev with a video for father's day from his daughter. A commercial has also been made at the ISS for a Japanese sports energizing drink. A cosmonaut takes hold of a floating bottle and drinks while looking at the Earth. Astronauts have played with Legos in space and read the periodical Popular Mechanics.

Cosmonauts do a Pepsi commercial during a spacewalk.

financed spacecraft took off and brought a test pilot to the outer limits of the atmosphere. According to their prognoses, paying customers will fly into orbit in the near future. And no pictures of exploding space shuttles can hinder this vision.

Professional astronauts, as many people expect, will be reduced to something akin to space bus drivers in the future. They will be transporting people and material there and back. They will assist scientists with carrying out experiments in orbital labs. And they will be the forerunners of the future journeys to the Moon and Mars.

President Bush announced that he wants to see human bases on other celestial bodies. Astronauts will come back to the Moon to build modest bases there, similar to scientific stations already existing on the Antarctic Continent.

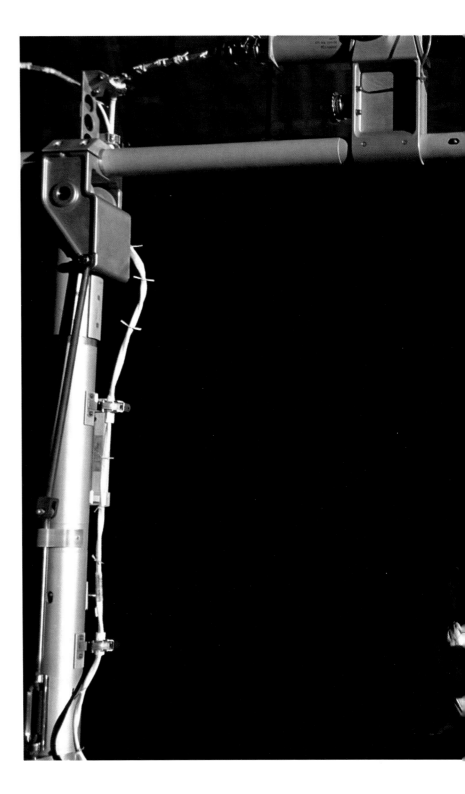

Kenneth Bowersox, during a spacewalk outside the ISS station in 2003.

The same would then take place on Mars' surface, even though the bases there will have to be somewhat bigger. This is how we like to perceive the role of astronauts: as trailblazers for future space settlements; astronauts as construction workers in the middle of nowhere. The only disappointment is that after more than forty years of manned space missions there is merely one station in operation which is not located on another planet but only in our own front yard.

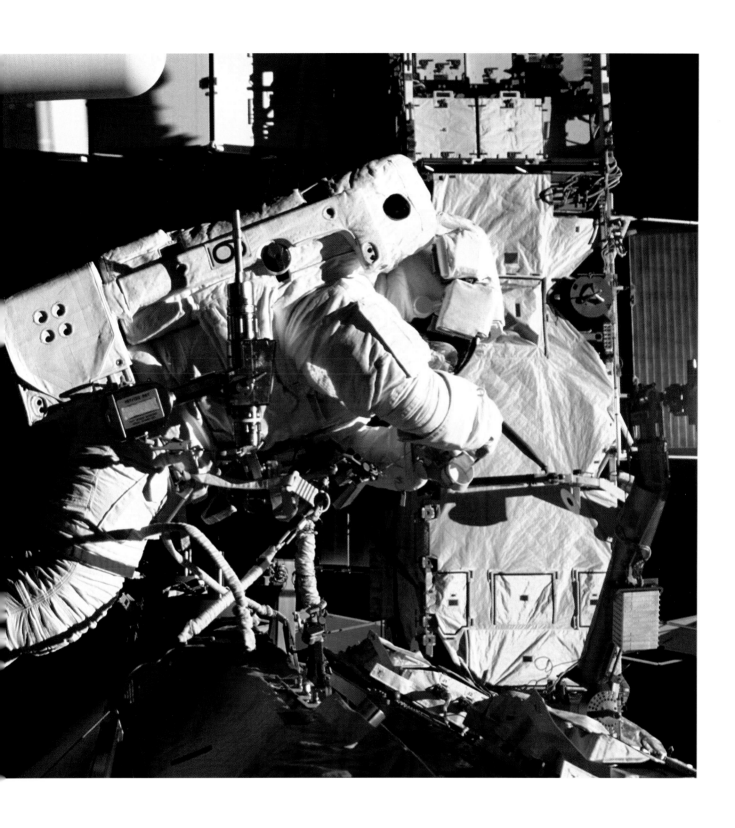

View from Space

This photograph shows the Earth as seen by the Apollo 8 mission astronauts on the way to the Moon, sometime around Christmas 1968. Never before had people been further from the Earth. For the very first time astronauts could see our planet as a whole entity.

Page 165:
Astronaut Donald Pettit waits with a camera in front of a porthole inside the ISS orbital station. He looks at Lanzarote, one of the Canary Islands.

If we wanted a definitive term, we would not refer to astronauts as space travelers. The diameter of the Earth is some twenty-seven thousand miles and during journeys to the moon people do not travel further than one mile short of the twenty-seven thousand. In reality, spacecrafts only float at the edge of the Earth's atmosphere. It takes them thirty minutes to make a full orbit of the planet. There are still scarce air particles in the regions where space stations orbit the earth. That leads to continuous minute collisions and extremely weak, but still undeniable slowing. Now and then the thruster rocket has to be ignited to propel the station into higher orbits.

At a distance of several hundred miles, the Earth can not be seen as a whole. The horizon is curved but our planet is so

Every one and a half hours, the astronauts can watch sun rise and sunset. This is one of the most splendid pictures of sunrise above the Earth, photographed from the Space Shuttle Atlantis in 2000. The sun casts its light upon a part of the spacecraft's tail or, aft fuselage, to be more precise.

The star-spangled sky as seen from the space shuttle; back on Earth, the scintillating of the stars is dimmed by the atmosphere. They sparkle with unhindered intensity in space. In this photograph, you can also see a part of the ISS.

close it fills the whole view out of a spacecraft's portholes. Only a handful of people have had the opportunity to get so far as to actually see our planet as a sphere in space. It was the Americans who traveled to the moon who had this unique chance at a distance of almost twenty seven thousand miles. It must have felt quite strange for them to see the whole Earth. They could make the blue planet with all the people they knew and their memories disappear from view with only one thumb. Few astronauts have been able to express clearly how it feels to see the Earth from space. The first view from a porthole shortly after the craft gets above the edge of the atmosphere must remain in one's mind forever. Those who are not to spend a long time in space try to spend every minute of their free time hanging around the craft's windows eager to brand the Earth's image into their brains. Just imagine, there are mountain ranges going by and cities that light up at night, jungles, deserts, oceans, the whole globe spins underneath you. Flashes of lightening, hurricanes, polar lights; astronauts can see it all from a unique perspective. Besides the splendor and the immense variety

on Earth, it is also its apparent fragility which deeply impresses. They can see that the atmosphere is merely a paper-thin layer of air which we pollute recklessly. Seen from space, countries and borders blend together; there are no walls, no border crossings and no fences. The feeling that Earth is but one immense organic entity eventually overwhelms every astronaut.

Sooner or later, all astronauts are asked whether their space adventure has in any way changed their lives. The answers of

Astronauts Michael Baker (left) and Tammy Jernigan while photographing Earth from the 'skylights' in the cockpit of the Space Shuttle Columbia in 1992.

This picture shows the Earth's horizon, as seen from one of the portholes of the ISS.

Sunrise above the southern hemisphere of Earth, seen during a combined space mission of American Apollo and Russian Soyuz capsule in July 1975.

Hurricane Elena photographed from the interior of the Space Shuttle Discovery in September 1985.

Who: *Story Musgrave,*USA
(1935)
When: 1983-1996

Why: *A distinct figure recognizable by his bald head, but remembered as a man of great knowledge, between 1958 and 1987 he studied math and statistics, management, chemistry, medicine, physiology and literature. He received academic degrees in all these fields. As a US marine, Musgrave piloted 160 different aircrafts; he obtained a flying instructor's license and worked as an airfreight pilot. He is an experienced parachutist and besides his regular job as an astronaut – selected in 1967 – he also worked as a part-time surgeon and university professor of physiology. Musgrave was a reserve crew member for a Skylab space station mission but his opportunity came only in 1983. He completed six shuttle flights between 1983 and 1996. He is the only astronaut to have flown in all five American Orbiters.*

Page 175:
This picture reveals tropical storm Sam raging in the Indian Ocean, seen during a space shuttle mission in January 1990.

The sun sets above the Sahara desert. At the time this picture was taken in 2002, Space Shuttle Endeavor was flying high above Sudan.

Page 175:
This picture shows a rather unusual view of a hurricane. This is the eye of hurricane Ivan as seen from above by astronauts of the ISS station. Ivan scourged the Caribbean region in the fall of 2004.

course differ from one individual to another. There are examples of astronauts who adapted a new attitude to the world as result of their space missions. For many the journey strengthened their religious beliefs. Some of them became evangelicals, while still others took to studying the paranormal. But the majority would claim that their space mission, and especially the delicate view of the Earth in the universe, played a crucial role in their spiritual development. It must, however, be said that many remained as stone sober as they were prior to their mission.

The majority of pictures of the Earth have been taken from unmanned satellites. Such records are much more useful for scientists because they are taken according to a precise pattern from precise angles and are thus not distorted or biased. Satellite pictures are also taken in all possible wavelengths:

A number of Greek islands with Crete left below, as seen from Space Shuttle Challenger in 1985.

Page 179:
This picture of the Kliukhevskoy Vulcan on the Kamchatka Peninsula in Siberia was taken at the end of 1994.

infrared, ultraviolet, etc. This allows scientists to retrieve more valuable information from the records. Astronauts often get requests to photograph certain locations, but at the end of the day these recordings lack a systematic approach. Thousands of pictures have so far been taken from manned spacecrafts. Sometimes the photographed location is identified only after the return to earth because it is rather difficult to pinpoint an exact place from an altitude of some 18,000 miles above the earth. A particular location will remain in focus for only a few seconds. Astronauts have detailed atlases available so that they can get more easily orientated.

After their return, astronauts have to submit their recordings to thorough examinations in lecturing halls where they are selected for permanent records. However, in a certain way it

Hurricane Florence as observed from the space shuttle. Florence swept through the Caribbean in September 2000.

Northern lights above Canada, photographed from the ISS in January 2003. The round shape below is the Manicouagan crater in Quebec where a meteor hit the Earth a long time ago.

Page 183:
Kennedy Space Center and its surroundings recorded by the space shuttle flying overhead in May 1989. You can see various launch pads as well as the runway. Titusville is left above and Cocoa Beach and Merritt Island are below in the middle.

This photo reveals aurora australis, the southern light, seen from the Space Shuttle Discovery in 1991. This phenomenon is produced by electropositive particles coming from the sun and colliding with oxygen and nitrogen molecules in our atmosphere.

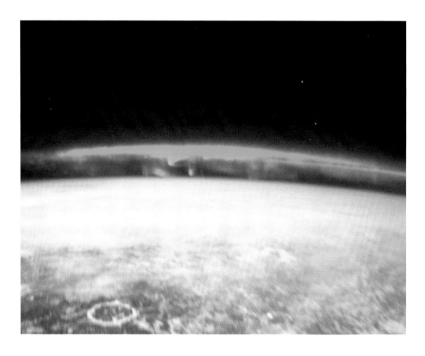

must be a strange, disconnected experience because the pictures are not so different from pictures taken on holiday sojourns. Certainly pictures of Earth taken from space do stimulate people's imaginations.

The west coast of the United States as seen from space shuttle in April 1990; the Salton Sea and Imperial Valley can be seen left below.

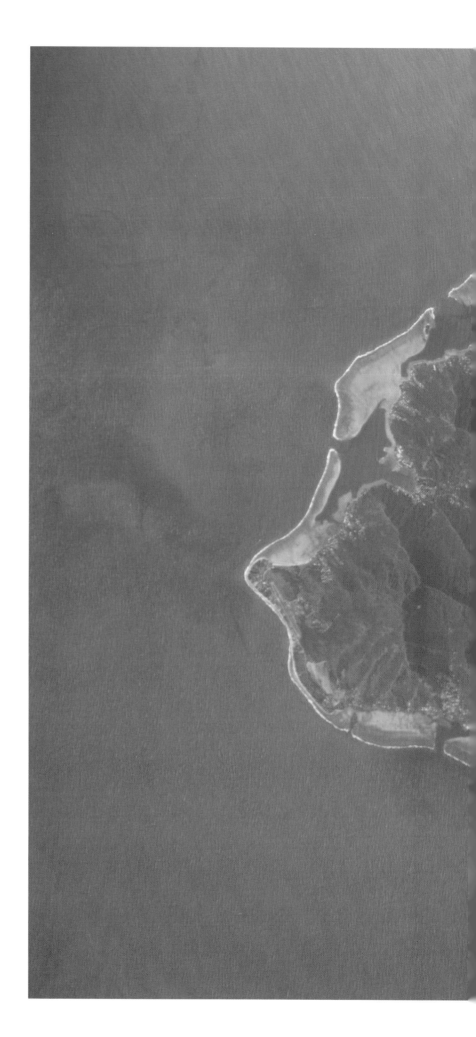

This is the small island Moorea in the south Pacific Ocean, photographed from the ISS in September 2003.

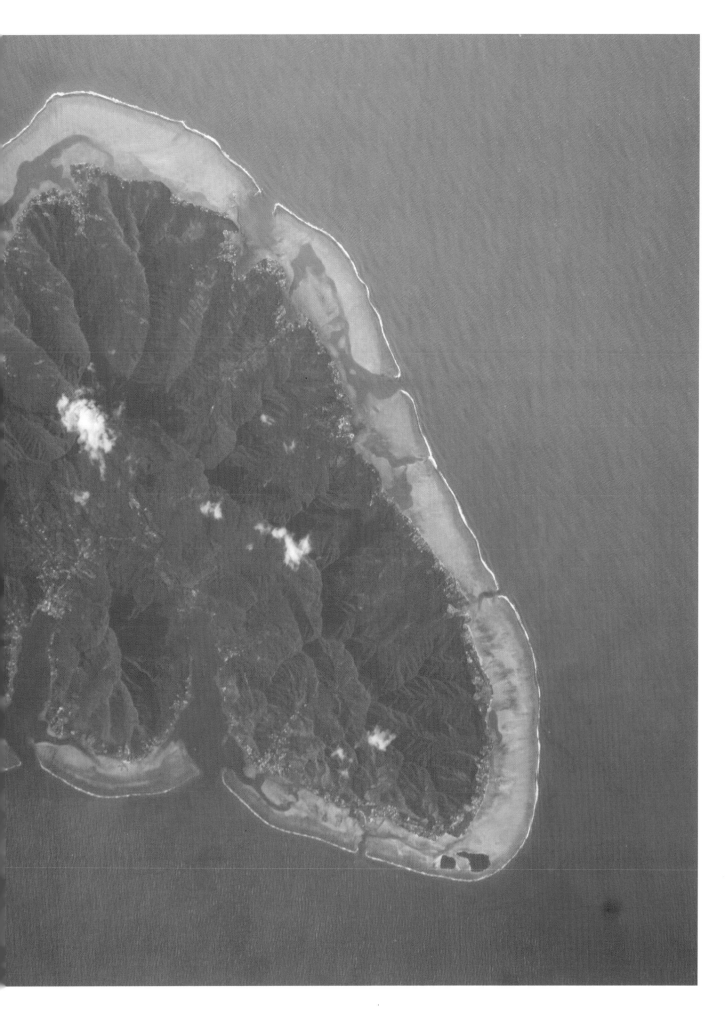

This is sunlight above the ocean. The photograph was taken from the space shuttle in
1990.

Page 187:
In this photo, the Space Shuttle Colombia flies
above the Great Lakes area along the border
between the United States and Canada. In the
middle is Lake Michigan.

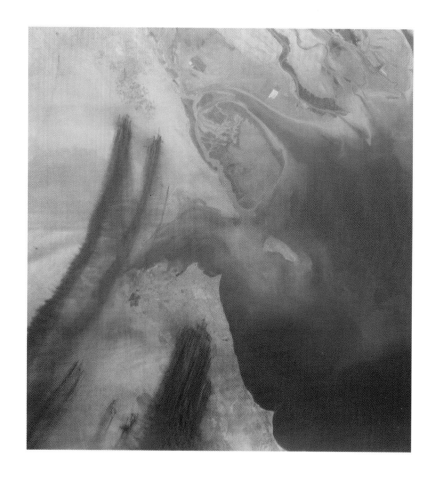

Smoke from the countless oil wells in Kuwait
in April 1991, seen from the space shuttle. Oil
wells north of the Bay of Kuwait and south of
the Kuwait City are on fire.

The volcano Etna in Sicily is about to explode at the end of 2002. This rare occurrence was clearly observed from the ISS station.

Part of the Himalayas as seen from the ISS. The high left peak is Makalu (27,762.5 feet or 8,462 meters above the sea level), on the right you can see Mount Everest (29,035.5 feet or 8,850 meters above the sea level) with clouds surrounding the top of the mountain. Most of the unmanned satellites have their cameras focused straight down which does not allow them to take pictures similar to this one.

Sunlight reflected in the Yellow River (Huangho) in China directly south of the Gobi Desert. The dark brown mountains in the photo are on average 2,300 feet high. The photo was taken by astronauts on the Space Shuttle Endeavor at the end of 1994.

This is the southern part of Greenland as seen from the space shuttle in 1992. This picture reveals the numerous fjords in the area. Almost continuously, massive parts of icebergs break off and then drift away, which can also be seen in this photograph. Only certain coastal areas of Greenland are inhabited.

This photograph shows the Middle East as seen by the crew of the Space Shuttle Columbia in February 2002. Astronauts often point out the fact that there are no borders visible from space. From orbit, the Earth is a homogeneous entity without borders.

Back to Earth

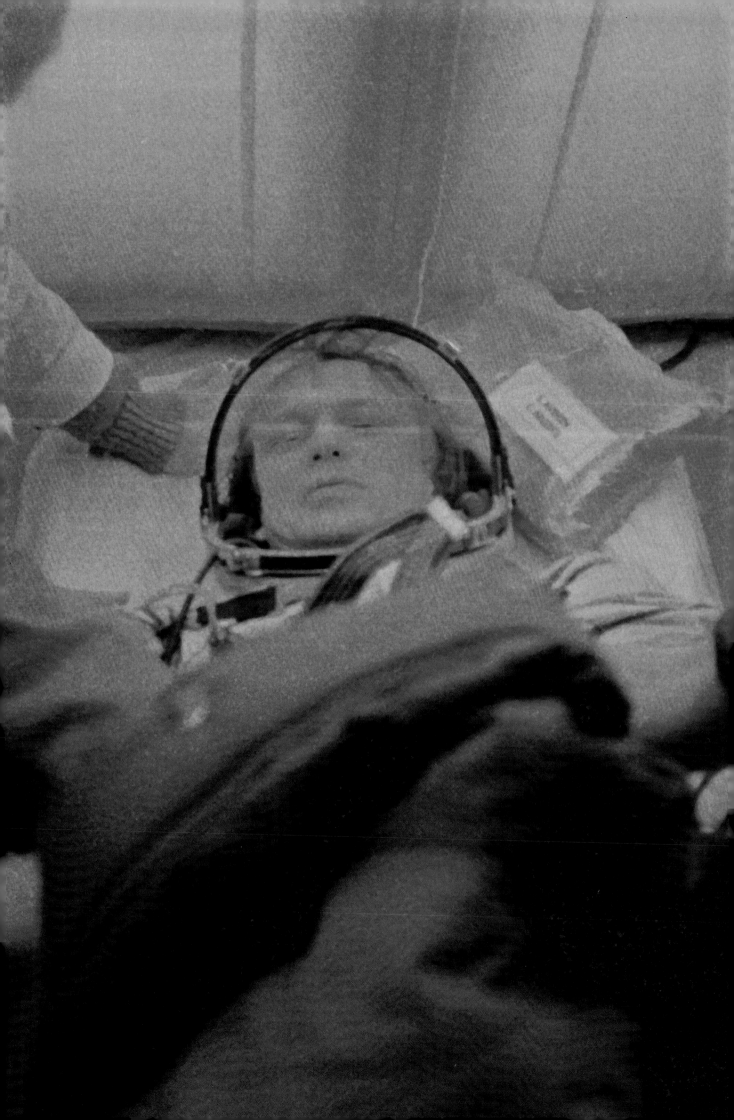

Back *to Earth*

A Soyuz capsule during its descent to Earth, the picture was taken above cloud cover. The moment its gigantic parachute opens up, the free fall of the capsule is finished and the crew inside is thrown with immense power in all directions – a shock comparable to that experienced by a bungee jumper on an elastic band.

A rocket's liftoff is a spectacular event accentuated by flames, smoke and the deafening roar of engines. At that moment, realizing that there are people inside the massive rocket is rather terrifying. Is there anything that could fail? Do they stand any chance? In this perception, the liftoff phase seems to be the most dangerous part of any space mission. However, if you take a look at the statistics, you realize that it is the landing which is the most risky. During a liftoff, astronauts rocket upwards in a huge launch vehicle but during landing they have to descend without the assistance of the rocket's engines. The risk that something could fail has proved very likely.

A spacecraft has only one attempt at landing. The rockets which bring the spacecraft into lower altitudes are ignited at a very precisely calculated moment so the space shuttle can make its descent into areas of greater atmospheric density where it gains speed. The re-entry into the atmosphere must

be done at a particular angle, which requires immense precision. If the angle is too acute, the G-force effect on the crew will have catastrophic consequences. Fortunately, astronauts do not have to do everything themselves because re-entry is, to a certain extent, pre-programmed on the shuttle's computers.

The Soyuz capsule comes down to the ground in the steppes of Kazakhstan. Shortly before the actual landing, small rockets are ignited which are designed to absorb the worst impact. As a side effect, the engines raise a cloud of dust. The force of the initial impact differs from landing to landing, but many cosmonauts compare it to a car crash. This photo was taken from a helicopter which circled around the landing capsule. Within a few minutes, the rescue team arrives at the place of landing to help the cosmonauts from the awkward position inside the cramped module.

Helicopters wait in the steppes of Kazakhstan to salvage the Soyuz capsule which has just landed. This picture was taken in February 1996. On board, there are Russian cosmonauts Avdeyev and Gidzenko together with German astronaut Reiter.

This is a photo of Umbert Guidoni, prior to his political career.

Higher politics

What would you do if your whole nation knew your name, your popularity had no limits and you wanted to commit your abilities to your country? You might choose to enter politics. That is what many astronauts have done, some of them with definitive success. The most famous example is John Glenn, senator for the state of Ohio between 1974 and 1999. But he was even more ambitious than that: in 1976 he was chosen as a candidate for vice-president under Jimmy Carter, but eventually he had to resign from the candidacy in favor of Walter Mondale. In 1984 he made a bid for the Democratic Presidential Nominee, but had to withdraw from the campaign with a considerable debt on his shoulders.

Between 1976 and 1982, Harrison Schmitt, the last man to set foot on the Moon, represented New Mexico in the Senate on behalf of the Republican Party. In November 1982, Apollo 13 astronaut John Swigert was elected into the House of Representatives but he died a month later – before he could swear the oath.

Also some Russian cosmonauts became involved in politics. Valentina Tereshkova, the world's first woman in space, reached the peak of her career in 1974 when she was appointed a member of the Presidium of the Supreme Soviet. Another Russian cosmonaut, Petr Klimuk became a member of the Central Committee of the Communist Party. Vitali Sevastyanov, Elena Kondakova, Svetlana Savitskaya and Gherman Titov got a seat in Duma, the Russian parliament in Moscow. Georgi Beregovoi, a cosmonaut of Ukrainian origin and consequently also a member of parliament, supported the young politician Viktor Yanukovitch who later became the controversial president of Ukraine. In 1968 and 1970, Yanukovitch was convicted in court of battery and assault – later on he was acquitted. Beregovoi spoke in his defense. In due time, cosmonaut Vladimir Dzhanibekov took a seat on an international committee which is currently trying to acquit the former Serbian president Slobodan Milosevic of the alleged war crimes accusations.

Then there is Vladimir Remek, who became the first Czech citizen in space in 1978 and who has recently been elected into the European Parliament on behalf of the Czech communist party. The Italian astronaut Umberto Guidoni's career took a similar course. His colleague Franco Malerba finished his term at that time and did not get re-elected. French Claudia Haignere, who made two flights to space, in 1996 and 2001, achieved the position of minister for research and consequently became minister for European Affairs in Chirac's government. Zhugderdemidiyn Gurragcha, the Mongolian pilot who spent a week as a guest in the Soviet orbital station Salyut 7 in 1978, held the position of the Minister of Defense in his land between the years 2000 and 2004.

The French astronaut Claudia Haignere is assisted out of a Soyuz capsule after its successful landing.

Once the last propelling rocket burns out, the ship will begin to freefall. Of course, it is a controlled free fall, because there is a trajectory which will bring it down to a predetermined location. Soyuz capsules land in the steppes of Kazakhstan;

Relief can be seen on the face of Claudie Haignere after she left her Soyuz capsule at the end of a fifteen-day long mission. The picture was taken in the steppes of Kazakhstan.

French cosmonaut Jean-Pierre Haignere, husband of Claudia, is back on Earth. Surrounded by rescue teams he is carried out of the Soyuz capsule.

Who: *Yuri Romanenko, Russia (1944)*

Where: *Mir*

When: *1987*

Why: *The flight control staff knew that they had to be careful with Yuri Romanenko. He was prone to losing his temper in even the slightest disagreements. For no legitimate reason whatsoever, he would see red all of a sudden and call his victim every bad name under the sun. During his long stay on the Mir he had many verbal conflicts with his flight controllers. He is notorious for a verbal attack against a researcher who dared to remind him that prior to his return to Earth he had to complete her experiment and pack up the pieces of equipment. From space he would command people who had no business in the control room to leave immediately. Visiting cosmonauts were instructed to remain on their guard and they observed him with ever greater distance. Strangely though, he is remembered as a lovable person by his colleagues.*

Page 201:
German Ulf Merbold recovers shortly after returning from a month long stay at the Mir station, in the fall 1994. It was his second space mission: in 1993 he was the first West European to fly in a space shuttle.

Dressed in warm clothes and surrounded by airlift team officials, Claudia Haignere recovers from landing after her second space mission during which she visited the ISS as the first European woman.

This picture reveals a general view of the landing site of a Soyuz flight in April 2004. In the foreground you can see American Mike Foale being interviewed by a journalist. In the middle,Russian Alexander Kaleri inside a thermal pack and behind, Dutchman Andre Kuipers. They are surrounded by military representatives, doctors and other officials. Behind them, there is the capsule which brought them back to Earth. A helicopter cruises above this landing site somewhere in the steppes of Kazakhstan.

space shuttles come down on the runway of Kennedy Space Center in Florida – and at times on another airbase in the US. But before the landing takes place an awful lot has to be done in space. Preparations for re-entry can take a day or even more. A spacecraft is used as a garbage truck; except

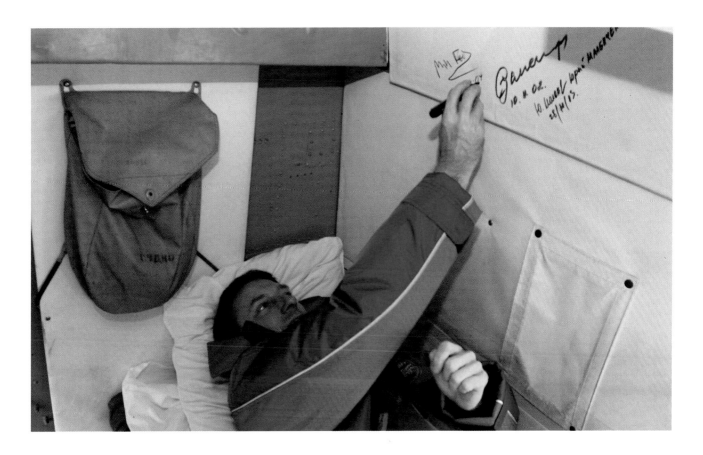

for the payload there are therefore also trash bags on board which a permanent space station wants to get rid of. Once all the baggage is on board, astronauts say their good-byes (preferably with a drink) to the permanent crew of the station. After all good-byes are said, space suits are put on which protect the crew from suffocating in case of substantial loss of pressure during the descent. Then the airlock of the station is closed. From that moment on, the spacecraft is

American Mike Foale autographs the coating of a helicopter which is going to transport him from the landing site in Kazakhstan. Foale has just returned from a stay in space which lasted 195 days.

Astronaut Mike Fincke gets out of a helicopter in October 2004 in which he flew from his landing site in the steppes of Kazakhstan to the city of Kustanay, a distance of two hours. He and his mission crew will be further examined there before returning to Moscow.

Immediately after their flight in 2002, Roberto Vittori and Yuri Gidzenko, dressed in the traditional Kazakh attire, are greeted by the authorities of Kazakhstan. Shortly afterwards they will fly to Moscow.

Who: *Sergey Avdeyev, Russia (1956)*

Where: *Mir*

When: *Since 1992*

Why: *He was the holder of the world record for longest amount of time in space: 747 days, more than two years of his life, accumulated during his three missions on board the Mir. In total, he made some twelve thousand orbits of the Earth. His longest stay lasted 379 days, much longer than originally planned. A paying foreign astronaut took his seat in a return flight. Avdeyev just felt like hanging around for a few more months.*

again an independent space ship. Undocking is carried out and the journey back may begin.

The space shuttle, at least the spacecraft-like part of it, also referred to as the Orbiter, turns back to Earth. The Soyuz-type capsule first falls apart into three. First the tail part, used to propel the module, is rejected. The front part, serving as living quarters, is also released. What remains is the middle part, the control and command module which shelters the three astronauts inside. It is a small capsule, as far as the interior is concerned, not bigger than a phone booth. The crew must remain there for one to three hours – as long as the descent back to Earth lasts.

Just like during the launch phase, the crew members feel somewhat heavier due to the fierce slowing down of the module's motion. The capsule is plunging downwards through the atmosphere at the speed of a thousand miles

A royal visitor comes to greet Belgian astronaut Frank de Winne who spent a week aboard the ISS on behalf of the European Space Agency. In this picture which was taken shortly after his landing in Kazakhstan at the end of 2002, he is congratulated by the Belgian crown prince Filip.

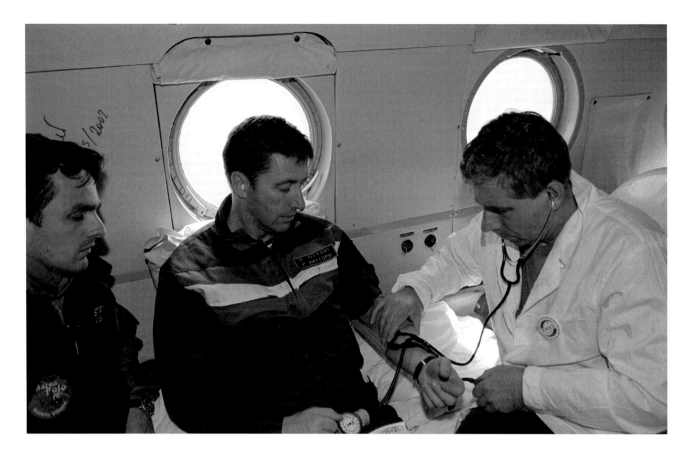

A physician takes Roberto Vittori's blood pressure on a plane heading from Kazakhstan to Moscow,

per hour and eventually comes to a standstill. The friction is so powerful that the air around the capsule turns orange and red. For a moment, no radio contact is possible because charged particles in the atmosphere distort the signal.

Astronauts' club

The Association of Space Explorers (ASE) is an elite club. You can become a member only on the condition that you have been in space. More than three hundred of them, from 29 countries, have joined the ASE. The organization was founded in 1985. The Association organizes a congress every year in a different country, where astronauts from all over can socialize. They meet to discuss serious issues, for example the question of how to convey the importance of manned space flights to general public. They also exchange practical as well as technical information. Each congress focuses on a different issue, such as manned space flights and the environment, education, culture and possible missions to Mars. But naturally, these get-togethers are also intended as social events. In a limited scope, the ASE also provides merchandise in the form of books and autographs. The Houston-based organization also serves as an agency which mediates the hiring of astronauts for various events (royalties start at 3000 USD).

There is yet another astronauts-only club: the rock-and-roll band 'Max Q', named after the moments at liftoff when the rocket is exposed to the strongest aerodynamic powers. 'Max Q' performs at all sorts of events which are associated with space exploration. The members of the band change from time to time but its very core stays the same: lead singer Carl Walz, Steve Robinson on guitar and Susan Helms on keyboard.

On page 207:

On his arrival in Moscow in August 1999, Sergey Avdeyev must be helped down the airplane steps. He has just finished his 188 days in space.

Like old American capsules from the sixties and seventies, the Soyuz lands by means of its parachutes. As soon as they open up, the capsule dangles on a strong elastic rope. The capsule shoots out into all directions only to settle its movements and descend to the ground in a stable manner. The cosmonauts are heavily rocked inside the module. Several seconds before touchdown, small rockets are ignited to make the final slowdown by creating a sort of invisible airbag. Nonetheless, cosmonauts often describe the moment of touchdown as being as strong as a heavy car crash.

Who: *Abdul Ahad Mohmand,*
Afghanistan
(1959)
Where: *Soyuz TM5*
When: *1988*

Who: *The first Afghan citizen to enter space, he spent one week there as a guest on the Russian Mir orbital station. He returned with an experienced cosmonaut, Vladimir Lyakhov in the Soyuz TM5 module. The return took a horrifying turn when the small rocket engines, which are designed to direct the capsule into the correct descent trajectory, stopped working properly. Some failed and others did not function long enough. They would have been directed towards China so the cosmonauts decided to cut the rest of the jets off. Afterwards, they had to wait for one long day in the tiny capsule before they got another chance. The last attempt was eventually successful; if it had not been, they would have got stuck in space. Mohmand, an Afghan air force colonel of a then Moscow oriented regime in Kabul, became a national hero. Later, he was forced to flee before advancing Mudjahedeen rebels. Together with his family he sought refuge in Germany where, among other jobs, he worked in a printing establishment.*

Renita Fincke, wife of American astronaut Mike Fincke, waits for her husband to return from Star City after a space mission. In the course of the mission, their daughter Tarali was born. At the time of this picture, she was four months old and had not yet seen her father.

Several times in the past, capsules strayed far away from their calculated landing spot. Cosmonauts had to wait quite long for rescue teams to arrive and provide an airlift. To avoid life threatening situations, cosmonauts had to go

Making a spectacular descent – here with astronaut Robert Crippen – the cockpit is brightly lit by the glow generated by the enormous heat released through friction around the Space Shuttle Orbiter.

Space Shuttle Discovery approaches the run-way at an airbase in California on November 17, 1989.

This photograph was taken from inside the Space Shuttle Challenger in 1985. It reveals a view approaching the runway at Edwards Air Force Base in California. The main objective at re-entry is to bring the space shuttles to a safe landing at Kennedy Space Center in Florida; however, at times weather conditions do not allow it. The Orbiter is then transported to Florida on the back of a Boeing 747, specially adapted for this purpose. In cases of emergency, space shuttles can land at other places around the world, such as airbases in Spain and Morocco. At every liftoff, those locations must be ready to receive the space shuttle, should circumstances require it. Sometimes a space shuttle liftoff from Florida has to be called off if the weather is too bad in Spain for example.

through survival training drills. In with the equipment there is a gun in case wild animals have to be deterred. In a few instances, the capsule has landed in a lake but fortunately the crews' lives were not put into jeopardy.

Astronauts for hire

Many (former) astronauts want to profit on the fame of their names by getting hired as speakers at congresses and similar events. Others try their luck as authors, painters or even poets. Naturally enough, most of them maintain their own web sites for business purposes where they boast of their past in space.

Edwin Aldrin: www.buzzaldrin.com
Jay Apt: www.orbitexperience.com
Alan Bean: www.alanbeangallery.com
Roberta Bondar (first Canadian woman in space): www.robertabondar.ca
Walter Cunningham: www.waltercunningham.com
Dick Gordon: www.dickgordon.com
Chris Hadfield (first Canadian to spacewalk): www.chrishadfield.ca
Mae Jemison: www.maejemison.com
Tom Henricks: www.starstruck.org
Ed Lu: www.edlu.com
Edgar Mitchell: www.edmitchellapollo14.com
Mike Mullane: www.mikemullane.com
Talgat Musabayev: www.musabayev.com
Story Musgrave: www.spacestory.com
Wally Schirra: www.wallyschirra.com
Rusty Schweickart: www.well.com/user/rs/index.html
Rick Searfoss: www.astronautspeaker.com
Al Worden: www.alworden.com

However, under normal circumstances, a descending capsule is located, while still in the air, from hovering helicopters. They land as soon as possible and put down a team of technicians, doctors and dignitaries who are there to take care of the crew. Cosmonauts are taken out of the capsule one by one and carried away on stretchers. The experience shows that especially after a long stay in space, cosmonauts are not strong enough in their legs to be able to walk unassisted. Once sitting on the stretchers, they get their first drink on Earth and are photographed and filmed by accompanying journalists. The first medical examinations take place in a makeshift tent after they write 'spasiba' (thanks) on the blackened capsule with a piece of chalk. Then they are transported by helicopter to the city of Kustanay (in the past they would fly to Baikonur, but that is a Russian enclave and the Kazakhs want their own stamp on space missions) where

After a five-day mission, the Space Shuttle Columbia lands at Edwards Air Force base in California. The picture was taken in November 1982. Two satellites were put into orbit during the flight. It was the first operational mission of a space shuttle type of spacecraft.

Shuttle commander Dick Covey waves from the cockpit of Endeavor after it safely touched down at Kennedy Space Center in December 1993. There were reasons for him to feel elated because his mission was exceptionally successful. In the course of five spacewalks, astronauts succeeded in repairing the Hubble Telescope.

they are welcomed in a Kazakh tradition – that is, dressed in appropriate attire. Then they travel by plane to Moscow. In Star City, they reunite with their families and are addressed in the theater building where they are warmly welcomed and receive praise in the presence of officials and dignitaries.

The Space Shuttle Atlantis makes a night landing at Kennedy Space Center in July 2001.

As for Americans, the procedure is rather different. The difference is noticeable at re-entry into the atmosphere. The space shuttle lands as one entity and no parts are lost. The thousands of heat-proof tiles on the belly of the orbiter must protect its crew as well as the spacecraft itself. Like a dive bomber, the space shuttle plunges downwards at an angle which is six times as acute as that of a civilian aircraft. The descent is so fast and the aerodynamics of the Orbiter

December 12, 1983: the ninth space shuttle mission. Six astronauts disembark from Columbia. It was the first flight for Spacelab and also the first flight of a West European astronaut, German astronaut Ulf Merbold.

such that it is impossible to change direction – and more than that, it is undesirable. The forces which work on the space shuttle make it uncontrollable for a human pilot. The descent trajectory of the shuttle is pre-programmed in the five on-board computers which are busier during this phase than at any other moment of its mission. To slow the ship down a bit, several huge loop maneuvers are pre-programmed so that the friction in the atmosphere can do its job. Up until a few minutes before the touchdown, all that the crew has to do is to keep their eyes on the computers

Autograph business

The prices which people are willing to pay out for an autograph of a famous astronaut or cosmonaut vary substantially: from tens to hundreds of American dollars. Based on experts' information, these are the most wanted samples:

1. Georgi Dobrovolski and Viktor Patsayev
   Two of the three cosmonauts who died during the re-entry phase in 1971. The third one, Vladislav Volkov handed out a large number of autographs during his life, which makes him irrelevant in this aspect.
2. Anatoli Levchenko
   In 1977, he was selected to pilot the Russian version of Space Shuttle called Buran but eventually lifted off in a Soyuz capsule and died a natural death eight months later.
3. Edward Givens
   The NASA astronaut who died in a car crash one year after he had been selected for a space mission in 1966; he had never been in space.
4. Theodore Freeman
   Chosen for a mission in 1963 and died in an airplane accident a year later.
5. Stephen Thorne
   Shuttle astronaut died a tragic death in a plane accident a year after his selection in 1985.
6. Clifton Williams
   He was selected for a space flight in 1963 and died in an accident in 1967. This man was a definite candidate for a moonwalk mission.
7. Charles Bassett
   He died in a crash on a jet fighter plane in 1966.
8. Roger Chaffee
   He died in 1967 during a fire onboard Apollo 1.
9. Elliott See
   He died together with Charles Bassett in the infamous plane crash.
10. Gregory Jarvis
    He died in the Challenger crash in 1986.

When you ask for it, most astronauts will provide you with an autograph. But some have obviously had enough. Neil Armstrong has not given a single autograph since 1994. Others, such as Edwin Aldrin, want to be paid for it. According to one autograph collector's website, he requires 250 American dollars for his signature and a hand-written reference to 'Apollo XI' and double the price if his signature should be placed on an object that has already been signed by others. For every other word written next to his autograph, Aldrin asks for 20 dollars.

and check if they work properly. The commander then takes over the 'flying brick' (one of the many nicknames for the space shuttle) to bring it manually down to the runway just like a normal aircraft. This is the only time during the mission when someone in fact pilots the ship. The last phase of the flight can actually be executed by the on-board computers but so far it has not once been necessary. There is no one in the steppes of Kazakhstan to see the Soyuz capsule coming down, unlike in Florida. There is a grand stand not far from the runway which seats the press and invitees. When the spacecraft touches down, it still takes some time for the crew to get out. The space shuttle is checked for poisonous gases. Only then can the crew members come out, one by one. On the runway they receive a welcome from a high-ranking NASA official—often the managing director of the

President Reagan and his wife Nancy give a red carpet reception to astronauts of the fourth space shuttle mission. It is not so common for presidents to see astronauts off or to welcome them back from their missions. There is always the possibility of a flight postponement for example due to bad weather, which means the President would have to go home or wait. President Clinton was the only one to risk visiting a liftoff: it was when the former Senator John Glenn was to fly into space in 1998.

Page 219:
Yet another ritual after landing: Commander
Frank Culbertson sprays the number '51' (refer-
ring to the STS 51 Shuttle mission) on the con-
crete of the runway at Kennedy Space Center.

This photo shows a tradition which takes
place immediately after every landing.
Astronauts walk around the spacecraft to
inspect the landing gear. Here, crew members
of a Discovery flight assess the damage after
having landed at Kennedy Space Center. The
bent figure is the flight's commander Tom
Henricks.

agency—in the case of a few special missions, the President has come. Traditionally, crew members walk around their spacecraft and inspect the underbelly as well as the wheels. Astronauts paint a circle on the runway exactly where the front wheel came to a standstill. Then reunions with families follow on the premises of the base.

The landing does not in the least mean the end of the mission. Especially astronauts who have stayed in space over a long period of time have to get re-conditioned to Earth. They are inclined to keep leaving things in the air around them as if they were still in zero-gravity. It is also not very practical to try to float out of your bed in the morning – you will end up falling down on the ground. Most of the effects of zero-gravity disappear once they return to Earth. The blood starts flowing normally again and the swelling of the head also quickly disappears. The same applies to the mus-

cles, which are much less strained in space. The decalcification of bones is irreversible as is the exposure to radiation. It is still not clear what the long term effects are in people who stay in space for long periods of time.

But these are not the primary things astronauts worry about. After they settle down a bit, there are endless meetings to evaluate the mission. Scientists receive the first results of their experiments. And then there are public appearances. Astronauts are image bearers, and an interview with an astronaut always attracts a great deal of attention. Here is the personification of the age of technology, a reason for you to be proud of your country. The first astronauts used to be received by heads of states as well as large masses of people. The Red Square in Moscow was crowded with people when Yuri Gagarin appeared with Khrushchev, the party leader. Cosmonauts used to travel around the world as representatives of the technological abilities of the

Who: *Jake Garn*, USA
(1932)

Where *Space Shuttle*

When: *1985*

Why: *Once chairman of the American Senate commission which is responsible for allocating money for the NASA space agency; after his flight in 1981, he said that he would love to get another chance to go into space. His wish was denied but Garn persisted and at the end of 1984 was asked by the contemporary NASA director to carry out an inspection in space. He was subjected to three days of thorough testing and then appointed to the crew. Within six months of his nomination, Garn flew into space. He participated in medical experiments but otherwise he did not do anything special and astronauts were maliciously delighted that he suffered from space sickness syndrome.*

Commander Bob Cabana hugs mission specialist Nancy Currie after their return to Earth
in December 1998.

Soviet Union. New York City celebrated the first astronauts
with a ticker-tape parade with cheering people greeting the
national heroes from New York skyscrapers. American astronauts also traveled the world receiving acclaim.
The first astronauts and cosmonauts were soldiers fighting
the Cold War without weapons. The idolatry and adoration

October 2002: cosmonaut Fyodor Yurchikhin has returned and is accompanied by his wife and children in Florida. Yurchikhin did not fly in a Soyuz capsule but he joined a space shuttle mission. The flight served mainly the goal of further extending the ISS orbital station.

Page 223:
Astronaut Shannon Lucid has President Clinton on the phone, immediately after she returned in September 1996. Lucid spent 188 days on the Mir and rightly became the female space-time record holder.

After having safely brought their space shuttle down at Kennedy Space Center, astronauts walk to an awaiting bus which will take them to the housing premises of the center. Meanwhile, the area below the spacecraft swarms with technicians and other staff.

was such that it would make pop stars jealous nowadays. In the Soviet Union the cult concentrated on Gagarin who died in 1968 and no one dared to cast any doubts on his status as a national hero – not even today. Rumors of his drinking, adultery, and allegations that his space mission did not in fact go well were always categorically dismissed. Only in the last few years did we learn that Gagarin was a human being

Michael Collins, Edwin Aldrich and Neil Armstrong are surrounded by enthusiasts during a ride through Mexico City, several months before the historic mission to the moon.

with human failings. However, none of it is mentioned in any of the various museums founded in his memory. In the building of RKA Energy, the biggest producer of Russian space equipment, there is an exact copy of Gagarin's work room as he left it when he departed for his, as it later turned out, fatal flight. His jacket hangs in the closet and the clock

One more journey around the world

After Apollo 11 astronauts came back from the first Moon landing in human history in July 1969, they made a world tour in the course of which they were received by statesmen and the general public in an unprecedented number of countries. They received one accolade after another and were cheered by crowds of at times hundreds of thousands of people and appeared on countless banquets as well as in public shows. Here follows the agenda of Neil Armstrong, Edwin Aldrin, Michael Collins and their wives: Mexico City (September 29-30); Bogotá, Columbia (September 30–October 1); Brasilia, Brazil (October 1), Buenos Aires, Argentine (October 1–2), Rio de Janeiro, Brazil (October 2-4); Las Palmas, Canary Island (October 4-6); Madrid, Spain (October 6-8); Paris, France (October 8–9); Amsterdam, the Netherlands (October 9); Brussels, Belgium (October 9–10); Oslo, Norway (October 10–12); Cologne, Bonn and Berlin, Germany (October 12–14); London, the United Kingdom (October 14–15); Rome and Vatican, Italy (October 15–16); Belgrade, former Yugoslavia (October 18-20); Ankara, Turkey (October 20-22); Kinshasa, Congo (October 22–24); Teheran, Iran (October 24–26); Bombay, India (October 26–27); Dacca, former East Pakistan (October 27-28); Bangkok, Thailand (October 28–31); Perth, Australia (October 31); Sydney, Australia (October 31–November 2); Agana, Guam (November 2-3); Seoul, South Korea (November 3–4); Tokyo, Japan (November 4–5); Elmendorf, Alaska (November 5) and Ottawa and Montreal, Canada (December 2–3).

stands showing the minute of his death. Baikonur can also boast of having an artifact from Gagarin's life: the house where he spent the night before the flight together with his stand-in, Gherman Titov. There is his bed, a jacket hanging in a display cabinet. Even today, cosmonauts respect the tradition and visit the house of their great forerunner. Idolization of Gagarin began while he was still alive. The idea of his second flight had to be abandoned because Nikita Khrushchev did not dare risk the life of his great hero and the nation's icon. Similar reasons led to the cancellation of the

Michael Foale, American of British origin is reunited with his family in October 1997 after four and a half months in space aboard the Russian Mir station. His wife Rhonda and his children Jenna and Ian accompany Foale who was temporarily seated in a wheelchair due to the necessary reconditioning to Earth's gravity.

In the photo below, John Glenn rides through Cocoa Beach shortly after he returned from his mission in 1962. The town is a spa situated close to Kennedy Space Center (at that time it was still called Cape Canaveral). Next to him you can see his wife Annie and (then vice-president) Lyndon B. Johnson. The photo on the right shows the 77-year old John Glenn waving to the crowds from a C-5 Corvette convertible during a parade along State Road A1A in Cocoa Beach, Florida after his second space mission, in December 1998.

second flight of John Glenn, the first American to enter space. He got his second chance only much later in his life.

Merchandising has always been big business with regard to astronauts. And that is true even with cosmonauts – whose faces appeared on countless stamps, buttons and paintings and other objects - generally in the form of the well-known

The plaque reads: "This Cherry Laurel tree was planted on October 16, 2001 By Astronauts JIM VOSS and SUSAN HELMS in commemoration of the Expedition 2 Crew's stay aboard the International Space Station"

style of socialistic-realistic art: retouched faces, undaunted looks, simple workers surrounded by ploughshares and countless flags with hammers and sickles. In the United States the souvenir shop at Kennedy Space Center is as big as a supermarket and you can only buy NASA certified products. It would not be America if there were no entrepreneurs eager to get their share. Everywhere around the launching base there are souvenir shops offering T-shirts, baseball caps and key chains. Portraits and books about the greatest accomplishments always sell very well.

This American ceremony in fact imitates a similar Russian tradition. After the return of a space station crew, the astronauts plant a tree on the premises of Johnson Space Center in Houston. Russians have been keeping this tradition since the very first space flight; that of Yuri Gagarin. Here you can see astronauts Jim Voss and Susan Helms digging.

Astronaut Mike Massimino greets the crowd that has gathered on the occasion of the welcome ceremony of space shuttle crew at Ellington air force base in the vicinity of Houston. This photo was recorded immediately after the spacecraft landed in March 2002. At such moments, NASA representatives commend their astronauts for their achievements. Once they finish, crew members take the floor to give a speech of their own.

Thomas Stafford, commander of the Apollo 10 mission, says goodbye to Snoopy, the mission's mascot, shortly before the liftoff.

Astronauts can live off their achievements for the rest of their lives. They remain interesting for autograph collectors as well as for authors of books about space exploration. Throughout their lives they are questioned about the time they spent in space regardless of what they did afterwards. There are astronauts who became university professors, congressmen, CEOs in corporations or even heads of NASA – but they all were remembered first of all

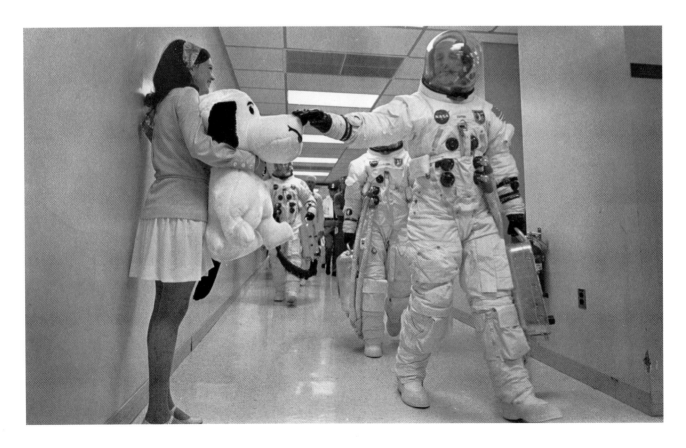

for their space adventures. Any organization that hires a former astronaut is aware of the fact that it wins a hardened and integral personality who is conditioned to working under pressure and at the same time he or she can serve as a highly-effective representative. There are examples of universities that gained considerable numbers of new students after they appointed astronauts as professors at their institutions.

... and Thomas Stafford, once again this time in 2002, photographed while standing by an Apollo capsule in the visitor's center of Kennedy Space Center.

In a hall in the central building of Star City, the last tributes are paid to Alexander Kramarenko, in the West a very little known Ukrainian cosmonaut who was selected for a space mission in 1965 but due to health complications had to wait for two years and only to be eventually left out completely. Nevertheless, he stayed to live and work in Star City. Kramarenko died of a heart attack at a train station.

In Russia, cosmonauts much more often remain in the space agency even after active service. Cosmonauts who do not stand a chance of another flight usually continue living in Star City. They become instructors for the new hires or they start working in management. We can speak of a very strict hierarchy here: famous cosmonauts from the early times of space traveling hold the highest positions. They also live in the biggest mansions and drive the fanciest cars.

Immortalized astronauts

An astronaut is a famous public figure. But some of them are naturally more famous than others and that fact is manifested in the number of objects that bear his or her name. And so, there are many schools in the United States that have been named after Christa McAuliffe, the teacher who died in the dreadful accident which claimed the lives of Challenger's crew. While John Glenn was still in space during his flight in 1962, a director of a school in Minnesota called a television station to report that his institution wished to be called the John Glenn Middle School. The School of Yang Li Wei, the first Chinese to fly into space, had previously been known as 'Secondary School Number 2' but now bears the name of its famous student. In Indiana, there is a school named after astronaut Jerry Ross who completed seven space missions. A scholarship at the University of West Virginia bears the name of Ronald McNair, one of the seven Challenger astronauts. The commander of the flight, Dick Scobee has post mortem become a name giver of a planetarium in San Pedro, Texas. There are still more interesting examples worth mentioning. A highway from Chicago to Detroit is called the Frank Borman Expressway, after the Apollo 8 mission astronaut. In Orlando, there is the John Young Parkway. Alan Shepard has a park in Cocoa Beach; Scott Carpenter has one in Boulder, Colorado and a public park in the town of Canton, Mississippi has been named after Columbia astronaut Michael Anderson. One of the NASA establishments bears the name of John Glenn; the swimming pool in Houston in which astronauts train for spacewalking is named after Sonny Carter, an astronaut who died in an airplane accident. Winston Scott, a space shuttle astronaut who carried out a number of spacewalks, gave his name to a pedestrian bridge over a Florida highway. The airport in the city of Longmont, Colorado bears the name of a former astronaut Vance Brand. In Ridder, a town in Kazakhstan, there is a Yuri Gagarin Orphanage. The birthplace of the first cosmonaut, the town of Gzhatsk was renamed after Gagarin. Kaplana Chawla, and astronaut of Indian origin who was killed in the Columbia crash, has been honored by Kaplana Chawla Way in Jackson Heights, a suburb of New York City with many Indian shops. Her name has also been given to a new super-computer in a NASA research center as well as to a new wing of a school in Ambala in India. Metsat, the first Indian satellite launched into orbit in 2002, has been renamed Kaplana-1. On top of it, there is a medical faculty with her name.

The honor is perhaps greater if your name is given to an object in nature. On the Moon, there are a number of craters which bear the names of different astronauts: Gagarin, Komarov, Tereshkova, Armstrong, Aldrin, Collins – and there are still more on the list. In 2004, three hills on the surface of Mars were named after three Apollo astronauts who died during their mission: Grissom, White and Chaffee. Seven other hills have been named after the astronauts who were killed in the crash of the Space Shuttle Columbia. These 'Columbia Hills' have their equivalent on Earth, the 13,976 feet (or 4,260 meters) high Columbia Point, a recently renamed mountain not far from Denver. Many astronauts have given their names to asteroids, large rocks orbiting around the sun. And as far as eternity is concerned, there are the Thunderbirds: Scott, Virgil, John, Gordon and Alan Tracy – all of them named after the first group of American astronauts.

Cosmonaut Pavel Belyayev, who died of disease in 1970, was laid to rest in the Star City cemetery. Most astronauts of good reputation have massive grave stones at the cemetery. Belyayev flew into space together with Alexei Leonov in 1965. Leonov performed the world's second spacewalk. He was the most experienced pilot of all in the first group of the Soviet cosmonauts. The plan was that he would fly to the Moon as the first citizen of the Soviet Union but the intention was abandoned later on.

There are innumerable examples of astronauts and cosmonauts who hit the skids after their missions however. They became frustrated and resigned because they could not get appointed for another mission (or even a regular flight), they took to drinking, cheated on their wives or disgraced themselves in other ways. Especially the astronauts who had received the greatest accolades often fell to the very bottom. Prior to their flights, they either had not been prepared at all or only insufficiently for the tumultuous welcome

The vast majority of American astronauts of military background are buried in the Arlington National Cemetery in Virginia. Stuart Roosa, a crew member of the Apollo 14 mission who died in 1994 is buried there.

Directly behind the Lenin Mausoleum on the Red Square in Moscow, is the Kremlin Wall where many heroes of the Soviet Union have been laid to honorable rest. The most prominent place belongs to the world's first cosmonaut, Yuri Gagarin, who died in 1968. In this photo, you can see Gagarin's tablet just to the right of the left guard of honor's head.

back to Earth and grew confused and did not know how to manage their lives surrounded by fame and splendor. Not everyone was able to adjust to a new life after being over-

Who: *Sultan Salman Al-Saud,*
            Saudi Arabia, (1956)
Where: *Space Shuttle*
When: *June 1985*

Why: *Saudi prince and businessman, he was invited by the Americans to be present during the unloading of a Saudi Arabian communication satellite. While staying in the USA for his training, the prince paid 1800 dollars per night for his hotel suite. He arrived at work in a limousine and was constantly accompanied by his bodyguards. He took a copy of the Koran to space with him and was exempted by religious authorities from the obligation to pray during his mission.*

The number of public appearances of the first generation of astronauts declines rapidly. No wonder: those surviving are now in their late seventies. In January 2004 five astronauts at the Kennedy Space Center were admitted to the U.S. Astronaut Hall of Fame. Less than sixty astronauts of importance are members of this hall of fame. A number of the first generation of former astronauts were present on this occasion.

John Glenn in 1962...

...John Glenn in 2004

Walter Schirra in 1962...

Scott Carpenter in 1960...

...Scott Carpenter in 2004

...Walter Schirra in 2004

Gordon Cooper in 1962...

Gordon Cooper in 2004

whelmed by fame and lifted on a pedestal as heroes of the nation.

Every astronaut puts up with life after a space mission in his or her own way. Some will continue to flirt with the idea of going back; others would rather not be questioned about it. Neil Armstrong, the first man on the Moon, belongs to the latter group. Now and then he agrees to appear for an official event, but generally speaking he avoids publicity. You

Lunatics

There is a group of people who claim with their eyes dry that the Apollo Lunar missions of the period 1969 to 1972 were all faked and the result of conspiracy. According to them, they all were arranged on a secret military base or in movie studios somewhere in Hollywood. The American government just had to triumph over the Soviet Union during the Cold War regardless of the financial consequences. It was only a successful Moon landing that could demonstrate the technological superiority of the United States. The need to stay on top was so pressing that the government decided to deceive virtually everyone. The launches of the Moon rockets were no doubt genuine but the astronauts did not get any further than the Earth's orbit. Pictures that followed afterwards were produced in television studios. The moon stones which were brought back to Earth were manufactured in ceramic ovens on earth.

NASA never knew precisely how to react to these claims. Of course they were dismissed as ridiculous, but how should they be opposed and denied? Silence only further strengthens the conspiracy theory because it looks as if the government is trying to keep something away from people. And if you react to those claims then you create the illusion that you take those lunatics seriously.

Is there any reason at all to assume that the Moon missions have never taken place? Supporters of the conspiracy theory base their claims mainly on thousands of photographs and videos that were taken over the course of the missions. They point mainly to the American flag which was hung out during the first landing in July 1969. In the recordings it can be clearly seen that the flag flaps as if there was a light breeze. But there is no air on the Moon. "Mistakes made by movie makers in a secret Hollywood studio," claim the conspiracy theory supporters. "Nonsense!", the only possible answer. On one side the flag had to be reinforced by an aluminum spring. When the flag was put into the ground, the flag mast and the spring were put into motion which caused the visible flaps.

Further on, the conspiracy theory supporters measured the length and direction of the shadows in the pictures and came to the conclusion that something was not right: some shadows were too short and others too long or they were not oriented in the right direction. According to NASA, it was caused by the angle at which those pictures were taken and at which you view the photographs. Just have a look at your holiday pictures and you will see that shadows there do not always correspond to the position of the sun in the sky. The third argument is the absence of stars in the pictures, while you could expect myriads of stars as a result of the lack of atmosphere around the Moon. This claim is very easy to refute: the sun (much stronger without the filter of Earth's atmosphere) had a blinding effect. However, more doubts exist: the Lunar landing module would have to tip over by the movements of astronauts inside; the astronauts would have to succumb to diseases caused by the cosmic radiation; and the best is that in 1967, NASA hired a hit-man to terminate three astronauts because they intended to write a book on The Great Conspiracy. That is how it usually is with scandalous claims: the further back in history they are the more absurd to the sober mind they become.

Dutch astronaut Wubbo Ockels takes his time shortly after landing in November 1985. His little son Martin sits by him.

can not really hold it against him; he has already been asked every conceivable question concerning his space mission. Edwin Aldrin has been involved in various plans for future space projects. Alan Bean found refuge in painting scenes from outer space; Harrison Schmitt became a senator and several other astronauts devoted their lives to religion or to the study of the paranormal. And all of them were confronted with people who were convinced that none of the three missions to the Moon had ever taken place. It is not long ago that Edwin Aldrin did a man over on the street who was a supporter of this conspiracy theory. Sometimes you just do not want to be reminded of the past in such way and especially not by an idiot.

Only a few astronauts are recognized on the street these days. Only in smaller countries do they have reason to excite a whole nation. In the seventies and eighties a number of pilots from the former East Block and other countries flew as guests with Soviet cosmonauts. They stayed in space only for a week or so and were not allowed to touch a single switch on the Soyuz capsule or in the orbital station, but once they were back home they were celebrated as if they had saved their country from impending doom. Stamps, shows, books, movies: all means were engaged to imbue the nation with the greatness of their achievements. Except for a very few, these guest cosmonauts faded into anonymity after the fall of the Iron Curtain.

Many astronauts have died. Not all of them have received honorable burial ceremonies since it does matter if you die while still in service or not. In the United States, astronauts with military rank are buried in the Arlington military cemetery in Virginia. Star City, near Moscow, has its own cemetery where many cosmonauts have been put to rest. The most beautiful monument that a cosmonaut can perhaps imagine is on Baikonur. Next to the hotel where cosmonauts spend the last few days before a mission, there is a small park with a view of the river Syr Darya. There are nameplates by the trees: each and every cosmonaut planted a tree here on the occasion of his or her flight. The tree of Yuri Gagarin is naturally the tallest of all and it seems certain that no tree will ever outgrow that of cosmonaut number one.

Space Tragedies

Space *Tragedies*

Astronauts of Apollo 1 mission pose for a photo in front of the launch tower on January 17, 1967, ten days before they lost their lives during a fire inside the capsule. The fire broke out in the course of a ground test.

A good method for fighting back fear is to gather information about the real risks and dangers that you are going to expose yourself to. The feeling of being in control of things which you fear is very important. Astronauts therefore want to know as much as possible about the equipment, people and procedures surrounding them. Provided that everything inspires confidence, astronauts can feel themselves at ease. That is what you constantly hear when astronauts talk about the dangers of their profession: they speak with respect about the work of technicians and the quality and reliability of the equipment they designed and constructed. What astronauts do as a matter of fact must seem like complete recklessness to an outsider: they get into something that is attached to the top of a rocket, have themselves launched into the atmosphere, orbit the Earth and return back in a falling ball of fire.

That may well be true, but it is certainly not what astronauts think. They believe in the pieces of equipment that surround them, often throughout their lives. They must have felt this confidence already as fighter jet pilots. An astronaut who gets scared out of his wits at every rattling sound cannot properly fulfill his role. Danger forms an integral part of their profession, every astronaut will tell you. All thinkable measures have already been taken to reduce the danger to the minimum, they will continue on and there is nothing else that can be done. Those who want to see and know the world around them will grow aware of the risk and expose themselves to the danger with confidence. And the danger that astronauts are exposed to is obvious: huge fuel tanks filled with extremely inflammable substances, roaring engines, glazing heat shields.

The number of astronauts that have been killed is not negligible: four Russians and fourteen Americans have been killed in the course of their missions. Three Americans and one Russian died during training. More than a half dozen astronauts died in

This group photo of Apollo 1 astronauts bears a special meaning because we know that at that moment their deaths were imminent. From left to right: Ed White, Gus Grissom and Roger Chaffee.

airplane accidents of some sort while on duty. What is most frustrating about these deaths is the fact that they could have been prevented. They died due to negligence, haste and misjudgments. Often it turns out that an accident is a result of extreme stress and pressure from the flight managers chased by ambitious politicians. Anyone who reviews the various tragedies in more than forty years of space exploration history can come to no other conclusion.

The first astronaut who died on duty remained unknown for a quarter of a century. Valentin Bondarenko was the youngest member of the space corps being trained in secret from 1960 on for the first manned space mission of the Soviet Union. On March 23, 1961, three weeks after he celebrated his twenty fourth birthday, Bondarenko was subjected to a test in a sound-proof pressurized cabin. The actual events of that day were unknown to the public until 1986 when the daily paper Izvestia finally received the necessary permission from the authorities to tell the story of the young cosmonaut trainee.

On that day, Bondarenko was going through his tenth day

Who:	Toyohiro Akiyama,
	Japan (1942)
Where:	Mir
When:	1990

Why: *The television reporter whose employer, TBS station, fixed him up with a one week stay at the Mir station which cost 28 million dollars, Mr. Akiyama was a passionate whiskey drinker and a chain-smoker. He was supposed to provide extensive coverage but instead spent most of his time in space sick, cringing in a corner even though later on he claimed that zero gravity had had felt like 'a transition into a new realm of sensual pleasure.' At a congress, he announced that he had had to throw up 17 minutes and 45 seconds after the liftoff and that it had not smelt or felt very good. Immediately after his return he asked for a massive meal. He wrote a book about his experiences in space but it has never been translated.*

Page 243:

The heavily damaged Apollo 1 capsule after it burnt up during the ground test. The three astronauts sitting inside at that time were all killed. An investigation showed that the capsule was designed and assembled with too much haste.

Astronauts of the nearly tragic Apollo 13 mission are received by President Nixon after their return to Earth.

Four Russian cosmonauts have so far been killed during space missions. From left to right: Vladimir Komarov, Georgi Dobrovolski, Vladislav Volkov and Viktor Patsayev. The history of Russian space exploration knows a great number of near-misses which could have had fatal consequences.

inside the pressurized cabin which was filled with air very rich in oxygen. After a number of medical tests, he removed the sensors attached to his body by means of special stickers. He smeared his arm with cotton drenched in alcohol. When he then threw it away it landed on a resistance wire of an electrical heater. In the oxygen enriched environment, the cotton bursts into flames immediately. In a fraction of a second, Bondarenko's woolen dress was in flames. Only after he had tried to extinguish the fire himself for some time did he decide to use the alarm. The doctor on duty rushed to the room where the pressurized cabin was located, but could do very little to help. It took a long time before he got the pressure inside to the same level as outside the cabin. Only then could Bondarenko be carried out.

The crew of the tragic Challenger mission as recorded during preparations for their flight. Left to right: Christa McAuliffe, Gregory Jarvis, Judith Resnik, Dick Scobee, Ronald Mc Nair, Mike Smith and Ellison Onizuka.

In 1984, a book by a Russian doctor who immigrated to the United States was published. This surgeon, one Vladimir Golyahkovski, in his book tells a story of a young cosmonaut, in the book referred to as Sergeyev, who died of wounds inflicted

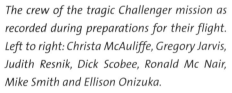

Christa McAuliffe has a fixed expression during a training session for her space flight in January 1986. The American teacher was chosen out of thousands of candidates to fly with the space shuttle and describe her experiences as a civilian – her account would have been intended for children mainly. McAuliffe joined the Challenger crew all of whom were killed by an immense explosion shortly after the liftoff. After this fatal accident, countless streets and schools across the USA were named after this teacher from Concord in Ohio. NASA completely halted all existing plans.

On April 29, 1986 the mortal remains of the Challenger crew are loaded on a cargo airplane at Kennedy Space Center to be transported to Dover Air Force Base in Delaware.

A part of the right wing of the Challenger is brought by USS Opportune at Kennedy Space Center after it was found by deep-sea divers miles off the coast. The wing was found 82 feet below the surface.

by fire. This story is in many points in agreement with the Izvestia article and so it was concluded that both texts describe the same accident. Golyahkovski's narrative contains more horrifying details. The doctor tells how while on duty in the Botkin Hospital, he was called by a military doctor, a Doctor Karpov, who announced that he was on the way with a seriously burnt patient. Moments later, a military ambulance arrived, followed

Most probably the last photo taken of the Challenger before it exploded. You can see flames shooting from the belly of the orbiter.

by a number of official cars with high-ranking officers inside. The patient was immediately carried to the first-aid ward.

Once he was examined, it turned out that the patient was burned all over. Skin, hair and eyes were all gone. However, the victim was still alive. The doctors were unable to find a vein for an injection except in his soles. He was given a morphine shot into his foot as well as other medicine. All in vain: sixteen hours after he had been admitted, he died. Golyahkovski never learnt the real name of the patient. Neither did he know who the young officer was who was standing by the telephone in the emergency ward and who apparently functioned as communicator between the hospital staff and the army officials who were waiting outside. For a short time the two of them discussed the circumstances of the horrifying accident. When the patient died, Golyahkovski said goodbye to the officer. Less then three weeks later, he read the man's name in the papers: it was Yuri Gagarin, the world's first astronaut. His flight turned out not to have been delayed in any way by the death of his colleague who had passed away such a short time before.

The second major accident in the history of space exploration could have been prevented if only the Russians had disclosed the drama of Bondarenko's death. The cosmonaut would have had much better chances if the air inside the pressurized cabin had not been so rich in oxygen: the flames would not have engulfed his body so quickly. Six years later, three American astronauts faced a similar fate. On January 27, 1967, three astronauts at Kennedy Space Center got into an Apollo capsule which attached to the top of a Saturnus 1B rocket. A month

Who: *Helen Sharman,*
the United Kingdom, (1963)
Where: *Mir*
When: *1991*

Why: *Twenty year old Sharman, a food-processing engineer working for the Mars snacks manufacturer, was chosen in 1991 out of thirteen thousand Britons to spend a week in the Mir orbital station. Russians were eager to take Westerners into space, for substantial sums of money of course – and Sharman's flight, not financed by the British government, was a nice opportunity to demonstrate their abilities. Until the very last moment it was not certain if the millions necessary for the flight would be available. Nevertheless, Sharman kept on training in Star City. Eventually, a Russian bank stood surety for the principal amount of the money and a number of sponsors also offered their financial help – among them a florist's. Scientists were not interested and so Sharman carried out mainly Russian experiments.*

Page 249:
Parts of Challenger which were lifted out of the Atlantic Ocean were eventually stored in an empty rocket silo at the Cape Canaveral Air Station, a military base located adjacent to Kennedy Space Center, the primary launch site.

later, Gus Grissom, Edward White and Roger Chaffee were to go into space and on that day they were scheduled to test the new Apollo Lunar capsule. This was a thorough test which was to take the whole morning. The hatch of the capsule was hermetically closed. Everything was ready but the simulation was not proceeding according to the plans; they were experiencing problems with communication. After more than five and a half hours, the voice of Roger Chaffee was heard from the radio: 'Fire! I can smell fire!' Immediately afterwards an announcement followed: 'Fire! There is a fire in the cockpit!'

Everything was happening way too fast. White found the handle which opened the hatch but the flames were spreading too quickly because the air inside contained one hundred percent oxygen – just as had been the case with Valentin Bondarenko a few years before. Technicians rushed to the scene but they knew that they could never succeed in reaching the astronauts in time. The pressure inside caused the top of the capsule to explode some sixteen seconds after Chaffee's first announcement. When the firemen looked into the capsule several minutes afterwards, they could hardly distinguish the dead astronaut's bodies from the interior. The temperature inside had been so high that their space suits had melted into the interior

One of the last pictures of Columbia before it exploded and fell apart. This photograph was made by means of a telescope based in New Mexico.

of the capsule. Later, it was made public that the most apparent cause of death was suffocation from the smoke inside. Three months after the accident, a three thousand page report was released. The real cause of the fire can not be identified with all certainty, but apparently it was a short circuit of the wiring inside. At many places, the wiring was installed so clumsily that an accident was surely inevitable. The quality control had much room for improvement. Researchers found a screwdriver stuck between two bundles of wiring which must have

Rick Husband, commander of the Columbia mission is ready to take off in his T38 jet fighter. The flight was carried out as part of preparations for his mission.

The crew of the Columbia spacecraft stands in front of a T38 jet fighter plane during one of their training sessions. Left to right: Rick Husband, Bill McCool, David Brown, Laurel Clark, Ilan Ramon (from Israel), Mike Anderson, ad Kaplana Chawla.

been dropped there by accident and which remained there even despite an official quality control. The pressure to finish work before the deadline set by President Kennedy – namely to have people on the Moon before 1970 - was so strong that it made some professionals cut corners. Americans were afraid that Russians would make it to the Moon first. The accident of Apollo 1 capsule paralyzed the lunar program for nearly two years.

In any case, the year 1967 would have been catastrophic. Three months after the fire of the Apollo 1 capsule it all went wrong for Soviet cosmonaut Vladimir Komarov, who was assigned to be the first to test the new Soyuz capsule. On April 23, Komarov was launched but after no more than fifteen orbits of Earth, the capsule began to rotate around its axis. Apparently one of the two solar panels did not fold out, which caused the posi-

Who: *Sergei Krikalev*, *Russia*
            (1958)
Where: *Mir*
When: *March 1992*

Why: *Thirty-four year old Krikalev flew into space in May 1991 for a stay on the Mir. He was in fact supposed to return only after several months but was later offered a possibility to stay longer because a visiting cosmonaut needed to return instead of Krikalev. He agreed. His decision brought him the status of the last Soviet citizen aboard Mir. While he was in space, the Soviet Union collapsed. The Community of Independent States was formed and due to an attempted coup, the Communist Party lost its integrity and Mikhail Gorbachov left high politics. Krikalev returned to Earth after ten months to a different country than he had left. Even the name of his birthplace, Leningrad, was different. The city was renamed Saint Petersburg. A documentary, "Out of the Present", was made about Krikalev's schizophrenic situation but he also served as inspiration for poems and even for an opera.*

tion control device to fail. The cosmonaut was not in a state to regain control over the capsule and the flight control center back on Earth could not help either. For hours, Komarov fought for his life. Eventually he succeeded in stabilizing the capsule and started to make the descent back to the atmosphere. But the capsule kept on rotating. The parachutes did not open and just like a meteor, the capsule sped down into the Kazakh steppes. The accident put an end to an incredible number of missions for the Soviet Union. The country plunged into mourning. Komarov's remains were put to rest in the Kremlin Wall, directly behind the Lenin Mausoleum. One year later, Yuri Gagarin, who got killed in a jet fighter accident, was also laid to rest there.

On June 30, 1971 an historic space mission of the Soviet Union was about to be completed. Three cosmonauts, Georgi Dobrovolski, Vladislav Volkov and Viktor Patsayev spent 2 days in the world's very first space station, Salyut 1. The Soviets lost the race to the Moon and decided to focus on a permanent

Israeli astronaut Ilan Ramon looks out of Columbia's porthole at the sun slowly rising above the horizon during his flight in February 2003. Ramon was killed during the re-entry together with six other crew members. Later on, fragments of Ramons' personal diary were found among other debris.

human presence in the Earth's orbit. The mission of these three cosmonauts, who managed to set the record time in space, was the first step in that direction. The three of them, seated in the Soyuz 11 capsule, successfully undocked the module from the space station and began to descend into the atmosphere. The capsule's parachutes opened up as intended and made a neat landing in Kazakhstan. The rescue team arrived within several minutes. When they opened the hatch of the capsule they found, to their utter dismay, three lifeless bodies. The shock was immense. An extensive ceremony on the Red Square followed. These three cosmonauts were also laid to rest in the Kremlin Wall. Manned space exploration came to a halt for a considerably long period of time. The Salyut 1 orbital station was never visited again.

A report showed that a valve in the capsule opened too early and allowed air to leak very quickly from the cabin. There was absolutely nothing the cosmonauts could have done about it. The accident could have been prevented if only the cosmo-

Seven Space Shuttle Columbia astronauts in February 2003, unaware of the fate they were to meet on their return. This picture was found on Earth on a film lying among other debris.

nauts' space suits were equipped with an independent source of oxygen. The interior of the Soyuz capsule was extremely small for three people and three cosmonauts with their space suits on could not fit inside and so the crew had only their woolen uniforms on. That changed with the next mission. Since that tragic accident, astronauts have always had space suits on during the descent. The introduction of this measure led to the reduction of the crew from three to two. Only in 1980 did Soviets dare to fly with three cosmonauts, however, the interior had to be redesigned.

For fifteen years, manned space mission were carried out without any fatal accident. According to many, it was a small miracle because in 1981 America introduced the space shuttle. It was a completely new type of spacecraft and its design was unlike anything that had flown into space before. The first 24 missions went off without any serious hitches. In 1985 it was predicted, that under good circumstances fifteen missions could be carried out in the following year and that that number would only increase in the years to come. There were even seats reserved for passengers. During the fifteenth space shuttle mission that was to be carried out in 1986 there was a teacher, Christa McAuliffe, on board. She had only minimum training. McAuliffe's presence on the spacecraft attracted enormous publicity. January is a cold month in Florida. That winter was so cold that there were icicles hanging down the launch pad construction. The flight was postponed several times, but on January 28 the flight control finally gave its consent. Never before had the space shuttle lifted off at such a low tempera-

Immediately after the tragic accident of Columbia, flowers were laid by the entrance of the NASA Johnson Space Center in Houston, the astronauts' headquarters.

This astronauts' memorial wall is located in the visitors' center at Kennedy Space Center. Flowers were laid there on the occasion of the ceremony of unveiling the names of the Columbia astronauts.

ture. Apart from McAuliffe, there were six other astronauts onboard the spacecraft. The space shuttle lifted off the launch pad and rocketed upwards. Then, some 73 seconds after the start, the shuttle suddenly exploded and split into pieces. Hundreds of invitees and thousands of spectators saw the spacecraft falling apart, countless fragments flying into all directions. The crew stood absolutely no chance. The United States saw the greatest tragedy in its history of space exploration. Many Americans still know where they were and what they did when this national symbol came to its horrifying end. Investigation proved that the Challenger should have never been launched. Several rubber insulation rings corroded due to the low ambient temperature and flew off the tank. As a result, explosive gasses started to leak from the tank, leading to the tragic explosion. It is not known how long the crew was aware of its inevitable end. The cockpit was found relatively intact on the ocean's floor. Apparently, immense aerodynamic force was fatal for the crew inside. There is no reason to believe that they remained conscious until the very end.

Apart from the technical investigation, the organizational issues were also thoroughly questioned. It turned out that the pressure on the NASA technicians and their vendors was way too high. The whole organization lost its credibility. It became apparent that trying to organize more than five flights per year was utterly irresponsible. It also turned out that manned space flights were not yet safe enough for civilians. From that tragic

mission on, no civilian astronauts have been allowed to travel into space.

The lessons learnt from the crash of Challenger remained forgotten until February 1, 2003. Seven astronauts of Space Shuttle Columbia – one Israeli citizen among them – were on their way back after a successful mission. Unexpectedly, their spacecraft broke apart during its red-hot descent. The crew died instantly. The underbelly of the space shuttle was damaged by a piece of foam which tore off from the main tank during the liftoff. This defect caused Columbia to lose its balance during the descent and not even the on-board computers could have managed to control the shuttle. The slightest deviation from the pre-calculated trajectory made the orbiter aerodynamically unstable. Extreme temperatures in combination with high speed caused the ship to explode. Once again, the American space program had to be stopped. Investigation showed that there was much room for improvement in the safety procedures of space shuttle missions. This time, NASA engineers took their time. Supply to the ISS had to be left to the Russian rockets. Only in 2005 could the shuttle program start anew.

The number of victims of the manned space exploration missions could have easily been much higher. Three astronauts of Apollo 13 mission could have died when an explosion occurred in their capsule on the way to the Moon. In 1975, two cosmonauts did not reach space because their rocket failed to work;

The countless fragments of Columbia were gathered and examined in a hangar. The debris was found on vast areas across the west and south of the United States. The limited number of the fragments collected means that the destruction of the exploded orbiter was total.

they touched down in a mountain range in Siberia not more than twenty minutes after the liftoff. In 1983, a Soyuz rocket exploded while still at the launch pad; the two cosmonauts who were inside managed to eject themselves by means of an emergency rocket. Vladimir Lyakhov and Abdul Mohmand could have died when the engine of their Soyuz capsule failed during the descent in 1988. In 1997, crew of the Mir station was in danger when a Progress cargo ship collided with the station. There are still more examples of terrifying moments caused by major or minor failings. They make it obvious that manned space exploration has not yet successfully gone through its testing period. Only professional astronauts may be exposed to such danger; we still can not be serious about the prospect of civilians flying into space – in spite of the recent initiatives of private American companies. Only professionals and a few very

Who: *Norman Thagard*, USA

(1943)

Where: *Mir*

When: *1995*

Why: *The first American astronaut to step onboard the Mir. He spent 115 days there. He was only partially able to carry out his scientific program because the launch of a new module with the equipment was postponed repeatedly. His Russian colleagues did not take their foreign guest (who had previously flown four space shuttle missions and was a truly experienced astronaut) seriously enough. Thagard was treated like a child by the authoritarian commander Dezhurov. He was hardly ever involved in important jobs. But above all, he felt he had been deserted by NASA in Moscow; they maintained very little communication with their man in Mir. Sometimes for days, he had no opportunity to speak English with anyone. Thagard complained about 'extreme cultural isolation'. His groundbreaking role as the first American onboard Mir certainly helped those who came after him.*

rich people can come into consideration for manned flights into space.

Civilian aeronautics went through a similar phase, but economic factors together with social need helped it to get over the most pressing problems. Twenty years after the Wright brothers, commercial airliners were already in operation. The number of airplane accidents is low and we do not hesitate to put our lives into the hands of civilian pilots. For the time being, the situation with manned space flights is quite different. Of course, there are countless civilians willing to undergo the risk of flying into space but there is no authority willing to accept the responsibility for their lives. Space exploration will yet remain in the hands of the military and astronauts will lose nothing of their immense appeal.

The Challenger broke into pieces 73 seconds after liftoff. It was to become one of the most penetrating images in modern history of the United States. Millions of television viewers watched as the symbol of the technological superiority of the USA exploded into thousands of fragments.

A Future in Space

A Future *in Space*

Orbiting the Earth, however fascinating it may seem, is not exactly how early generations of astronauts imagined the future of their profession. The idea that astronauts are explorers is deeply incorporated in our minds. It was President Bush in 2004 who announced that he would once again concentrate resources on exploration of other planets. From that moment on, all efforts of NASA should be focused in that one direction. First of all back to the Moon, then a Mars manned mission and perhaps other flights also to asteroids – immense pieces of rock which orbit the sun. These plans were received with varied enthusiasm. Not everyone is happy about the prospect of these manned space missions, one of the main reasons being the fact that they will be horribly expensive. Efforts should concentrate mainly on the assembly of the ISS which is at the moment far from complete. Meanwhile, it has turned out that the visions of President Bush will not be implemented soon but the program will no doubt receive substantially more money so that true space exploration can finally begin.

It is therefore possible that future astronauts will explore virgin territories. Americans have in total landed six times on the Moon but their radius of action on the Moon was very limited. There is a whole world waiting to be explored. In the first instance, the plan is to build an independent station on the Moon, similar to those already existing on the Antarctic continent. It will serve as the home base for future mining activities on the Moon. In the Moon's ground, there are considerable amounts of helium 3, an element which can be used in nuclear fusion – provided that it will ever be won from the Moon's ground. There is also oxygen in the ground, certainly in bounded form. It is also very probable that there is water in the form of ice under the ground on both of Moon's poles. Theoretically, there are thus materials that can be used for producing rocket fuel on the Moon. There are metals to be found on the Moon as well. In short, there are building materials which can be utilized for human presence as well as for construction of a spacecraft that would transport people to Mars, which would be the next stop. To sum it up, not everything that Moon inhabitants will need must be transported from Earth.

The dark side of the Moon is not influenced by the electromagnetic radiation of the Earth which means that it could serve as

Future moon travelers stand on the edge of a valley, as imagined by painter Pat Rawlings.

For the first time since the Apollo missions, a man-made object makes its descent to the moon's surface. As far as President Bush is concerned, return of manned spacecraft to the Moon is the main objective for Americans for the near future.

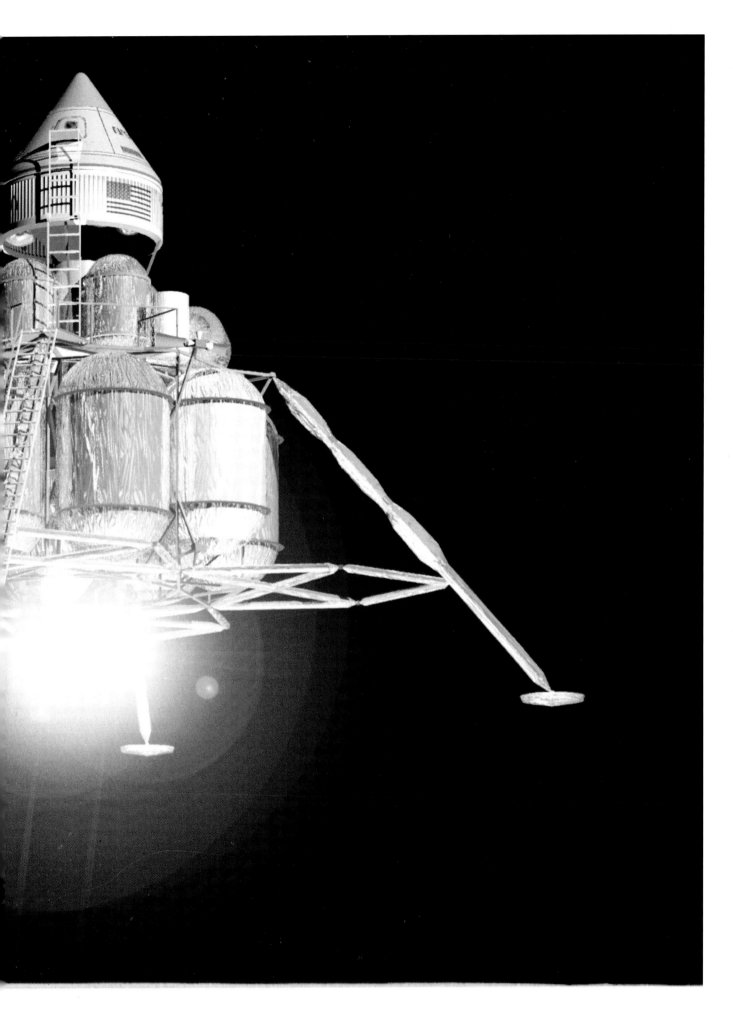

This picture reveals the implementation of a Moon base project. The living and working quarters are covered with a thick layer of moon dust to protect the inhabitants from space radiation, ultraviolet radiation coming from the sun as well as against substantial fluctuations in temperature. A large solar-panel field on the right supplies the base with electricity. Electromagnetic cannon will be designed for sending containers of Moon ground samples back to Earth.

an ideal location for a radio telescope. The Moon's surface is definitely not what we would call a friendly environment; you can not go out without a space suit. In the shade it is extremely cold, in the sun it is boiling hot. Due to the absence of atmosphere, the Moon's surface is completely exposed to space and ultraviolet radiation.

But the relative closeness to Earth makes the Moon an attractive destination. Not only for Americans; during the Cold War era,

Living in a wheel

In 1952, five years before the Soviet Union launched into space the world's first man-made satellite, Wernher von Braun (the father of the V-2 rocket from the era of the WWII and later an important figure in the background of the Apollo lunar landings) cooperated on a series of articles in Collier's, the popular science magazine, on the future of people in space. A gigantic space station was central in Von Braun's plans. This wheel-shaped station, more than 225 feet in diameter, was supposed to provide housing for hundreds of people and, according to plans, it would create artificial gravity by its slow rotation. The crew would, just like laundry in a washing machine, be pressed to the outer wall of the station. They would not have to deal with zero-gravity problems.

A similar station would be orbiting the Earth as early as 1963 Von Braun claimed in Collier's – later he changed it to 1967. But already some time before his death in 1976, Von Braun realized that reality was significantly more complicated than his imagination. After the Moon landings, the will of the American government to spend billions of dollars on costly space projects vanished.

But there was one man who was not deterred by this fact. His name was Gerard O'Neill, a professor of physics at Princeton University. O'Neill saw the importance to humankind in exploring other parts of the universe. To relieve the world's growing population, millions of people would eventually have to leave Earth and build colonies in space.

O'Neill made plans of gigantic floating space cities. In the middle of the nineties, that is within twenty years from the time O'Neill was making his plans, a sphere-like 'Island 1' would be built which could accommodate tens of thousands of earthlings. Whole villages, wildlife and agricultural areas would be located at the outer part of the rotating sphere. Its diameter was planned to be 1380 feet, its total weight: 3.5 million tons, 7500 times that of the complete ISS station.

O'Neill counted even the smallest of details. 'The equator of the sphere looks like the ideal place for a small river', he wrote in a 1976 book which was to become the classic text of space exploration, 'which would at certain points broaden into swimming pools. Along the banks of the stream, beaches could be made from Moon sand and at a certain distance, there could be foot and bike trails.' And Island 1 was to be merely the first of an armada of space cities – all wheel-shaped – and colonies flying to the Moon and Mars.

Gerard O'Neill did not live long enough to see his dreams come true. He would have surely watched the developments in the construction of our only existing space station with immense anger and impatience. Currently, the size of the quarters seems to be limited by the size of the space shuttle's payload bay. That also dictates the shape of the cylinder-like modules which can certainly not be designed to be bigger than a big mobile home. If a space city is ever built, it will be done gradually, module by module.

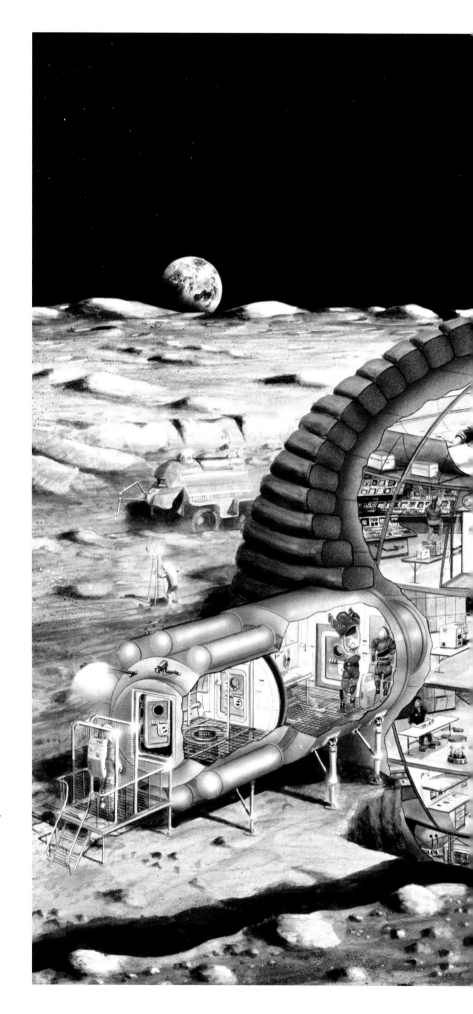

This picture shows a futuristic vision of a Moon base as designed by NASA engineers. According to the designers, an inflatable module 48 feet in diameter would provide shelter for twelve astronauts.

Soviets did make serious – though unsuccessful – attempts to carry out a flight to the Moon. Currently it is China that is beginning to attract attention. The country claims to have ambitions to build and maintain a base on the Moon in the future. This is a good reason for Americans to stretch their muscles and avoid being left behind. A return to the Moon will have to make more sense than the historic but rather modest six Apollo landings.

Who: *Vasili Tsibliyev, Russia (1954)*

Where: *Mir*

When: *1997*

Why: *Beyond any doubt, Tsibliyev is one of the most experienced and reliable astronauts. While he served as Mir commander he had to face an improbable number of difficulties. All of a sudden, pieces of equipment would fail to function, such as oxygen supply, nitrogen dioxide filters and the main on-board computer. Tsibliyev and his board engineer Alexander Lazutkin had to use all their wits to contain the perilous situations, for example when fire broke out onboard and the whole interior turned black from the smoke. At one point in time, Lazutkin by accident disconnected the wrong plug which resulted in electricity supply failure and the loss of balance of the whole station. To top it all, an approaching Progress rocket with a scientific module onboard crashed into the Mir. The damage was considerable and it seemed that the orbital station would have to be evacuated. All this stress and pressure led to cardiac arrhythmia in commander Tsibliyev. The flight mission control and flight management was far from supportive towards the cosmonauts; in fact they more or less blamed both men for all the problems. Once back on Earth, Tsibliyev had to defend himself and his conduct at a press conference. His days as a cosmonaut were numbered. Nevertheless, several days later he was assigned the function of the head of the training center for cosmonauts in Star City.*

People will have to stay there for months in a row and will have to build a functional infrastructure there. Just as astronauts are currently busy assembling the orbital station circling around the Earth, construction workers will have to put up structures and roads on the Moon. There are not yet official plans for it, but there are lobby clubs that advocate future Moon missions. Complex studies are being done on all the pros and cons of operating a moon base. The extent and number of details is striking;

Hopefully, people will not have to take so much risk on Mars: a descent from a vertical rock wall in a valley. Painter Pat Rawlings can nonetheless very well picture situations of this kind.

According to Pat Rawlings, huge oxygen production facilities will be standing on the moon in foreseeable future – they will be similar to this one which stands between two solar panel fields. Oxygen is an important element in rocket fuel and can be later used for a journey to Mars.

for example, they have already looked into how much toilet paper the future moon pioneers will need.

Naturally enough, there are people who look even further into the future. Apart from mining and astronomy there is yet another line of business which could be carried out on the Moon – tourism. In his book 'The Fall of Moon Dust', Arthur C. Clark let people sail through seas of moon dust onboard a sort of vessel. The desolate landscape with its flatlands, craters and mountains could certainly present irresistible attraction to countless tourists, who are bored by the landscape on Earth. In the long run, the prospect of building a hotel on the Moon could attract attention. The Moon hotel's guests could enjoy all the specific delights of the very specific place. Because the Moon is much smaller than Earth the gravity there is felt with much less inten-

sity. On the Moon you would weigh six times less than you weigh on Earth. If someone jumped off a springboard into a swimming pool he could, on his way down, do all sorts of crazy stunts. Thanks to the absence of air resistance, you would be able to send your ball miles away on a Moon golf course. For a tourist who has already seen everything on Earth, the Moon will become the ultimate destination. The first travel guide for the Moon has already been written.

Tourism is not an option on Mars jet. At best, Mars is located more than 37 million miles from Earth but the planet can get as far as 270 million miles away. An expedition to Mars would take from two to three years. However, as far as climate is concerned Mars is much friendlier than the Moon. On average the temperature is in the region of 13 degrees Fahrenheit below zero, which is not unendurable for the human organism. Still, it requires more than a regular warm winter jacket. The planet does have an atmosphere but people can not breathe it because it is too thin and contains a too high concentration of carbon dioxide. A space suit with an oxygen supply is therefore a must, just like on the Moon. What makes Mars attractive is the possible presence of water there. There are clear indications that at one point in time there must have been flowing water on Mars. According to measurements of unmanned probes sent to the planet, there is ice in the ground close to the North Pole. From water, frozen or not, hydrogen, an important element of rocket fuel, can be synthesized.

Not all supplies and materials necessary for Mars explorers must therefore be transported from Earth. A Mars base

This is a concept of a future Moon vehicle with two astronauts exploring the surface. The painting was commissioned by NASA.

could in the long run be largely self-sufficient. Astronauts could even cultivate their own crops and accumulate their own drinking water. Besides, astronauts would be carrying out important research because Mars is still an unknown and mysterious planet. What is more, there is still the pressing and unanswered question of if there has ever been life on Mars. The planet as we see it to a large extent looks like Earth had in earlier stages. A number of unmanned robots which have landed on Mars in recent few years are in fact doing the preparatory work for a future manned mission. Scientists would like to determine which areas and locations are most interesting – and at the same time safest – with regard to a future human presence.

There are still some serious obstacles on the way from Earth to Mars. There is, for example, the very real danger that astronauts would suffer from space radiation. This radiation originates in deep space and is diverted from Earth by its magnetic field. The spacecraft's coating would not be able to protect the crew. Nobody currently knows what the effects on the human organism would be. Simulation of space radiation

This is an imagined first small settlement on Mars, consisting of a landing module (in the foreground) and a vehicle for exploration of the surroundings.

Who: *Wendy Lawrence, USA*
(1959)
Where: *Mir*
When: *1997*

Why: *The first astronaut whose height disqualified her for a space mission; in 1997, Lawrence had already once been in space onboard a space shuttle and in 1996 she started to train for a planned four months stay aboard the Mir station. In Moscow, she was already established as one of the leading figures in the American camp who participated on the coordination of Mir flights. In 1997, a Progress cargo ship crashed into the Mir and it became apparent that a fresh American newcomer had to carry out a number of spacewalks and repair the inflicted damages. Lawrence had absolutely no experience with open space reparations. And there was yet another problem: with her height of five feet three inches, she was simply not tall enough to fit into the Russian Orlan space suit normally used by Russians for spacewalks. All of a sudden, Lawrence could forget about staying for long onboard the Mir orbital station; she was ordered to stop training and on her name was on the list was replaced by David Wolf. She found herself in the same boat with astronaut Scott Parazynski who after profound consideration was also not allowed to stay in Mir due to his height – he was too tall to fit into the Russian space suit. The couple was later referred to by their colleagues as 'Too Short' and 'Too Tall'.*

This picture offers a vision of two of the future Mars explorers standing by a jeep designed for exploration of areas around a virtual Mars base.

caused serious damage to the brains of rodents. Scientists are afraid of possible irreversible degenerative effects on genetic material as well as of carcinogenic effects. Periodical sun storms (every eleven years) present another obstacle. There are immense flames shooting into space and also a large number of powerfully charged elements emitted. These sun storms distort radio signals on Earth, which would make an expedition to Mars a very unwise idea at that time. Protective shields would certainly help but there are limitations to the thickness of armor plates of a spacecraft.

There are also physiological limitations which we should better take into consideration. Earlier in this book we mentioned decalcification and muscular atrophy in astronauts. During a journey to Mars, which would last much longer than an average stay in a space station orbiting around Earth, astronauts would have to spend much time and energy on keeping themselves fit in order to prevent the worst of these effects. There are plans of a space-

This picture reveals a vision of an airplane flying through a canyon on Mars.

craft which would consist of two modules linked together and would create artificial gravity power by rotating around its axis. But this plan still seems to be a little bit over the top right now. Then there is the real chance that someone will be affected by acute appendicitis or some other ailment which requires immediate help. Hospitals are millions of miles away. What to do? Nobody has a solution yet, except for the simplest one: Mars explorers would have to be in the best shape at the time of their departure. Of course, there will be a physician onboard but he or she would have only basic equipment. Consultations with Earth would also be very difficult because it take some twenty minutes before signal broadcast from Mars reached Earth.

Here we touch upon another sensitive issue: that of the mental health of the astronauts. From an orbital station Earth seems to be within a stone's throw. On the way to Mars, Earth would soon be seen as mere contours and eventually it would be only a blue point in space, just as Mars is a red star in the sky.

A normal conversation with your beloved ones would be basically impossible due to the time a radio signal needs to bridge the immense distance. The question has been raised if people should be sent to Mars with their relatives. Some say that a Mars mission crew must consist of couples but that could cause problems with regard to possible arguments and quarrels. Conflicts do in any way present a great danger when considering a Mars mission. The chance conflicts would come up are very real; hardly anyone can cohabit for two to three years and keep all the problems away. A conflict-free environment is certainly not possible. The Mars explorers would have to be improbably tolerant of one another.

Who: *Gennady Strekalov,*
Russia, (1940 – 2004)

Where: *Mir*

When: *1995*

Why: *Would the gentlemen cosmonauts be so kind and carry out a spacewalk and repair some equipment out there? was the appeal of the flight control directed to Gennady Strekalov and Vladimir Dezhurov who were at that time staying on board the Mir. Forget about it, snapped back the older of the two. He simply did not see any sense in it. The necessary equipment was not onboard and if something went wrong there was only this American visiting astronaut Thagard sitting at the flight controls inside. Nothing could soften Strekalov's attitude. His colleague was rather unhappy about the situation. He could see the storm coming: due to this willful disobedience he, as the flight's commander, would never be allowed to fly another space mission. The conflict hung in the air for two days. Then the flight control finally gave in: the spacewalk would not be carried out. The cosmonauts were fined nine thousand dollars each, but later on they managed to get the fine cancelled. Dezhurov still works in the Russian space corps, Strekalov died in December 2004.*

Were severe conflict to occur, it would be impossible to isolate the aggressors and keep them outside the group until the problem was solved. Entertainment would also be vitally important: books, DVDs, games. The absence of earthly 'stuff' (many astronauts report that while in space they missed the sounds of birds, flowing water, wind and the smell of flowers etc.) would be much more pressing than with people who merely orbit the Earth for several months. Well yes, supporters of the Mars mission idea claim, but there were sailors in our history that had to spend months at sea without having the slightest idea of where they were going. Those people were also stuck in a mentally-challenging situation, but that did not keep them at home.

This is how Pat Rawlings imagined a manned Mars spacecraft while descending to the surface of the Red Planet. The parachutes must be much larger than those used for descents to Earth because the atmosphere on Mars is much thinner.

A Chronology of Space Exploration

A **Chronology** of Space Exploration

This chapter offers an overview of the most important milestones in the history of manned space flights.

Yuri Gagarin

April 12, 1961

Yuri Gagarin becomes the first man in space. Seated in a one person Vostok capsule he orbits the Earth for the first time. After 108 minutes he lands safely in the steppes of Kazakhstan. It is the start of a legend that lives on till this day: Gagarin becomes an undisputed hero, honored all over the world. In 1968 he dies in an airplane accident. In a museum in Star City near Moscow, you can see his scorched personal belongings that have been put on display as well as a container with a ground sample from the very site where Gagarin and his instructor Seryogin crashed the plane.

A stereotypical image of astronauts: handsome, beefy men dressed in awkward space suits. This picture reveals the first group of American astronauts, the Mercury Seven. They were introduced to the press and the general public in April 1959. It was hoped they would catch up with the technological lead of the Soviet Union which at that time had already brought its first satellite as well as the first animal (a small dog called Laika) into space. But the Americans were not yet ready, and in 1961 Yuri Gagarin became the first man in space. The Mercury astronauts were constantly being outrun by their Soviet counterparts; the Soviets were the ones to stay longer in space, to carry out the first double flight and to put the first woman into space.

The first Soviet cosmonauts: a substantial number of them never made it to space and their names vanished. It was many years before the Russians disclosed the names of those who had never got the chance. Some were injured; others were dismissed due to disorderly behavior or were killed in accidents. This photo is a retouched version; the unworthy were erased. Yuri Gagarin is in the first row, fourth from the left.

May 5, 1961

Alan Shepard in his Mercury capsule makes a 'frog's leap' into space. He does not yet make a full orbit of the Earth. After a quarter of an hour or so he returns. Shepard is received as a hero but can not reverse the fact that the United States missed the third major achievement (after the first Sputnik satellite and the little dog Laika as the first animal in space in 1957)

Alan Shepard, the first American in space, is examined by doctors prior to his launch on May 5, 1961.

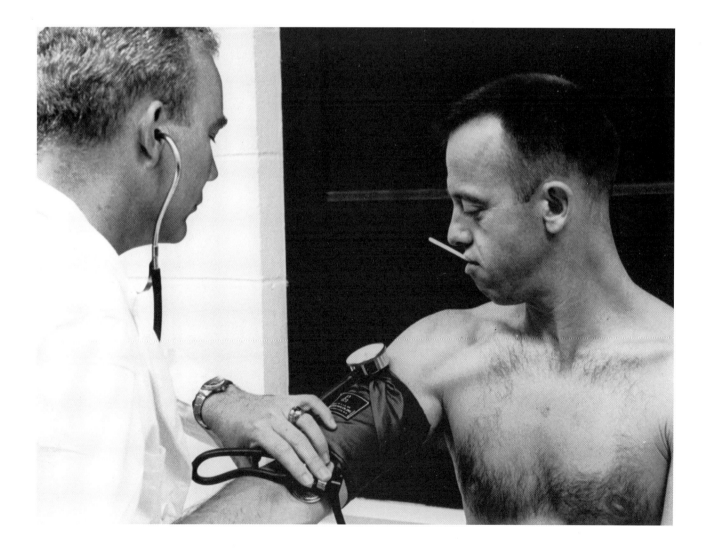

Alan Shepard seated in his Mercury capsule.

Gus Grissom, the second American to reach the outer limits of the atmosphere in a Mercury module, eating his breakfast before his launch attempt on July 19, 1961. The flight was cancelled that day due to unfavorable weather conditions. His liftoff took place two days later.

August 6-7, 1961

Gherman Titov, the second Soviet Union cosmonaut, makes seventeen full orbits of the Earth and remains more than twenty-four hours in space. The United States could compete only with the mini space flights of Shepard and Grissom (who makes a similar space jump in July 1961).

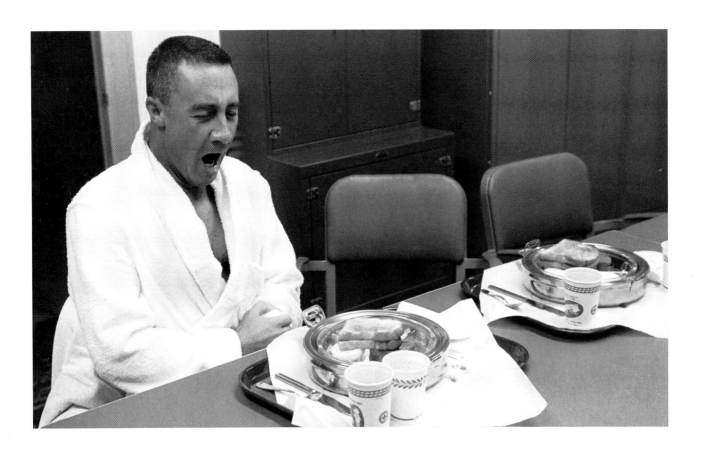

February 20, 1962

At last, an American orbits the Earth: it is John Glenn. After some five hours, he lands safely in the Atlantic Ocean where he is airlifted by helicopter. He receives unprecedented honors. Glenn is the most charismatic of the seven Mercury astronauts. He will use this gift for his political ambitions and career later on. President Kennedy forbids him to make another flight to space. The same measure was taken by party leader Khrushchev with regard to Yuri Gagarin. Glenn as a symbol of space exploration becomes too valuable to be lost.

This photo shows the liftoff with John Glen aboard in 1962. Until the era of space shuttles, astronauts were launched in small capsules integrated into the top section of the booster rockets.

August 5-11, 1962

The Soviets achieve yet another primacy: they launch two Vostok capsules within one day. In history, it is recorded as the first double space flight. Cosmonauts Andrian Nikolayev and Pavel Popovich fly within 4.5 miles of each other.

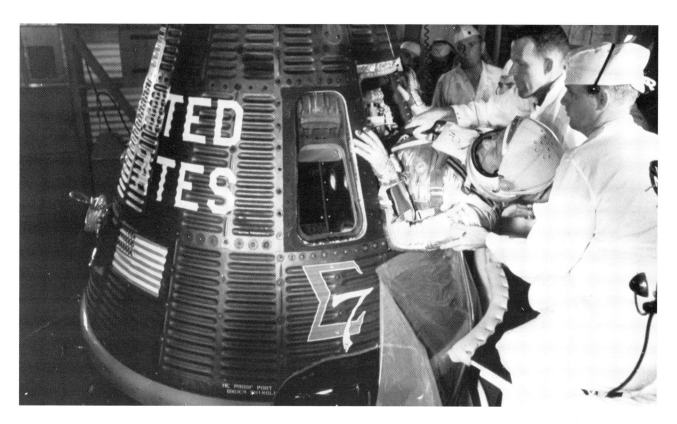

Mercury capsules from the sixties were no bigger than a phone booth. Astronaut Walter Schirra is helped by his colleague Gordon Cooper aboard the capsule for the launch on October 3, 1962.

Astronaut Gordon Cooper jogs on Cape Canaveral beach in Florida before his flight in May 1963. In the background are launch pads under construction.

June 16-19, 1963

Valentina Tereshkova becomes the first woman to fly into space. Her background is wholly in agreement with the communist tradition. An ordinary textile factory worker, she has no experience with flying, except for a couple of parachute jumps. Later she will (as arranged by Mr. Khrushchev) marry another cosmonaut, Andrian Nikolayev. From this later divorced marriage a child is born, also after some insistence of the Communist Party leadership. Her daughter Yelena became a medical doctor.

Valentina Tereshkova

Page 297:
Gemini 7 as seen from Gemini 6 on December
15, 1965. That was the first time two American
manned capsules were simultaneously in
space.

October 12-13, 1964

Three cosmonauts fly in one spacecraft: Voshkod 1, which is in fact an extended Vostok. The interior of the capsule is so confined that they can not wear space suits but have to carry out the mission dressed in vests and trousers.

March 18-19, 1965

Alexei Leonov becomes the first cosmonaut ever to take a spacewalk. Dressed in a space suit he leaves the Voshkod 2 capsule with Pavel Belyayev on board. The seat of the third cosmonaut is occupied by the necessary airlock. Leonov remains in outer space for ten minutes. He will later reflect on his experience as a successful space scenery painter.

March 23, 1965

Gemini 5 astronauts Gordon Cooper and Charles Conrad get ready for their launch on August 21, 1965.

Gus Grissom and John Young fly in a Gemini capsule three times around the Earth. It is the first American space mission with more than one person on board. The Gemini project serves as a test for Apollo, the Moon landing program which was launched by President Kennedy. He wished the project to reach its climax in the first Moon landing before 1970. Unknown amounts of money were released for the project.

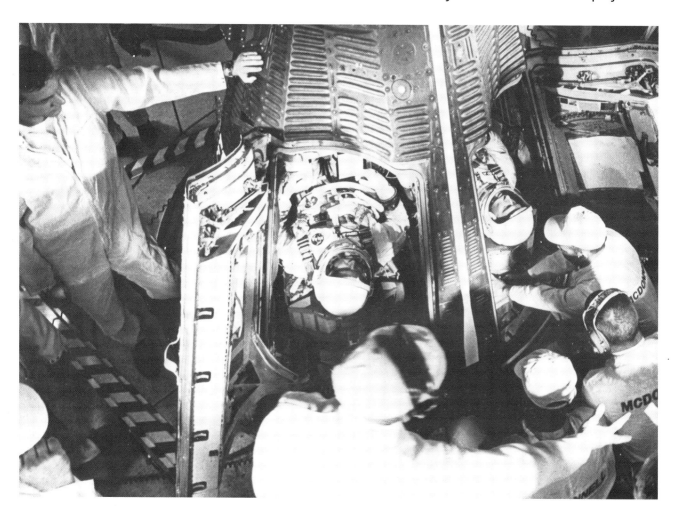

June 3-7, 1965

The first American to experience spacewalking: Edward White stays outside the Gemini 4 capsule for 21 minutes. His colleague Jim McDivitt observes him from inside the module.

Edward White photographed during his spacewalk. Clearly visible is the open airlock in the capsule.

Mercury, Gemini and Apollo capsules land in the ocean in calculated locations. The astronauts and the capsules are picked up by helicopters and transported to an aircraft carrier adapted especially for rescue action of this kind. Here, the return of Gemini 6 in December 1965. In the background is the USS Wasp.

January 27, 1967

American astronauts Grissom, White and Chaffee are killed in a fire in their Apollo 1 capsule during a ground test. The space program is delayed considerably.

April 23-24, 1967

Cosmonaut Vladimir Komarov crashes during his return to Earth when the parachutes of his capsule get tangled up. There were serious problems with balance control on the spacecraft during his flight.

October 11-22, 1968

Americans finish the preparations for their lunar landing missions. In the Earth's orbit, three astronauts test the Apollo 7 capsule.

December 21-27, 1968

For the first time ever, people depart in the direction of the Moon. In the Apollo 8 capsule, three American astronauts make ten orbits of the Moon. At Christmas, they take turns reading aloud from the Book of Genesis.

Apollo 8 crew (among them William Anders, Jim Lovell and Frank Borman) in a simulator on Earth, one month before their flight to the Moon's orbit in December 1968.

January 14-18, 1969

For the first time in history, the Soviets succeed in docking two manned spacecrafts together. In the first module there is one cosmonaut, in the other there are three on board. Two of them go 'out' into the first spacecraft and then they return to Earth in it.

July 16-24, 1969

After two more Apollo orbital flights around the moon, the time came for Apollo 11 mission with Neil Armstrong, Edwin Aldrin and Michael Collins on board. Armstrong and Aldrin land on the Moon on July 20 and seven hours later, they go outside. In total, they spend more than two and a half hours outside the Eagle lunar module. During their triumphant journey around the world they visited dozens of different countries. The Americans were finally satisfied with their achievement; they felt that in the space exploration race they had at last caught up with the Russians. They had feared that the Soviets would land on the Moon before them but years later it turned out that their obscure Moon landing program was a complete failure. The gigantic N-1 rocket designed and built for that purpose exploded during a launch test.

The American flag on the Moon seen from the lunar module Eagle in which Neil Armstrong and Edwin Aldrin landed in the 'Sea of Stillness'.

October 11-18, 1969

For the first time, there are three manned spacecrafts in Earth's orbit: Soyuz 6, 7 and 8. They do not perform docking experiments but carry out space maneuvers together which bring them as close as several hundred feet from one another.

April 11-17, 1970

The third Moon flight nearly ends up in catastrophe. On the way to the Moon, an explosion occurs on board the Apollo 13 capsule. A landing becomes impossible. The three astronauts manage to secure the electricity and oxygen supply systems of the attached lunar module.

After landing on Earth, astronauts of Apollo 11 had to spend three weeks in quarantine. The danger that they could have been contaminated while on the Moon's surface was negligible – and soon it was proved so. Here wives of the astronauts stand by a window of the quarantine room. Shortly afterwards they became part of an unprecedented media attention: astronauts were welcomed as heroes all around the world.

Launch of Apollo 15, July 1971

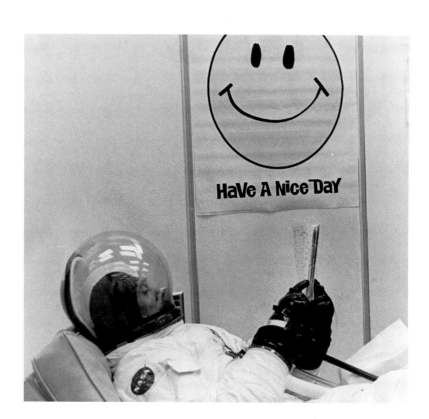

Astronaut Charles Duke has a last look into
the mission plan for the Apollo 16 mission.

June 6-28, 1971

Cosmonauts Volkov, Dobrovolski and Patsayev are killed when internal pressure drops suddenly in their Soyuz 11 capsule during the re-entry. The trio had carried out a successful mission in the world's first orbital space station, Salyut 1. Much later, chilling pictures were released showing the rescue team trying to resuscitate the three cosmonauts.

December 7-19, 1972

Gene Cernan (left) and Harrison Schmitt, during the Apollo 17 flight; it was the very last Moon mission. The photo was taken by Ron Evans, the third crew member, who orbited the Moon while his colleagues walked its surface.

Apollo 17 becomes the sixth and the last lunar landing mission. One of the two astronauts who land on the Moon's surface is Harrison Schmitt, a geologist. Other Moon flights that were initially planned had to be cancelled due to insufficient financial resources as well as lack of general public interest. The American public had another priority at that time: the Vietnam War.

The last Moon flight; the crew of Apollo 17 is picked up. The USS Ticonderoga waits in the background.

This picture shows the American Skylab space station which orbited the Earth in the early seventies and accommodated three crew members. Skylab was partially assembled from redundant parts from the Apollo project. In the background is the Amazon River in Brazil.

May 14, 1973

The Americans launch Skylab, their first space station. It has been assembled from redundant Apollo project modules. Three astronauts spent 84 days on board Skylab. This record remained valid until Americans started their long-term stays on board the Russian Mir orbital station. But nobody in 1973 thought such cooperation would take place.

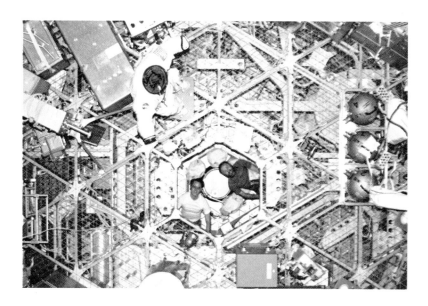

Astronaut Bill Pogue took this picture of his crewmates Jerry Carr (right) and Ed Gibson on board the space station Skylab during its last manned flight.

Astronaut Jerry Carr balances his colleague Bill Pogue on the tip of his finger during the last Skylab mission.

1974

After ten long years of effort, the Soviets finally abandon their plans to build a rocket which would bring their astronauts to the moon. The program was bedeviled by bad luck. All four test launches of the immense N-1 rocket from Baikonur which had been organized from 1969 went wrong. The longest flight lasted 107 seconds. The 315 feet tall N-1 rocket is the biggest rocket ever built by the Soviet Union.

July 15-24, 1975

Three Americans and two Soviet cosmonauts meet in space. An Apollo and a Soyuz capsule dock with each other and courtesies were exchanged for two days. It is the last time an Apollo module reaches space.

March 2-10, 1978

Czechoslovakian pilot Vladimir Remek flies as a guest into space on board a Soyuz capsule and boards the Salyut 6 space station. Remek is the first non-Soviet/non-American in space. He remains on board for a week and carries out various experiments on behalf of his country. The next few years will see visiting cosmonauts from nearly all Eastern Block countries. In this way, they all created their new national heroes who were associated with the superiority of the Moscow government.

April 12-14, 1981

John Young and Robert Crippen fly onboard the first space shuttle craft and complete a 54-hour test mission in space. It is the very first time that a winged spacecraft is launched. The space shuttle was a completely new type of spacecraft when compared to capsules that had been used before. The airplane-like, winged Orbiter could be used again as well as both main booster rockets. Dozens of flights per year were predicted but over time this estimate proved too optimistic.

April 19, 1982

The Soviets launch Salyut 7, a space station which can remain operational for much longer than the previous manned Salyut orbital stations. For shorter or longer time, dozens of cosmonauts flew to stay at this station. The Salyut 7 was as big as a mobile home.

November 11-16, 1982

After four test flights, the first operational space shuttle mission is successfully carried out. Two communication satellites are unloaded from the shuttle's payload bay. Small propelling rockets transport the man-made satellites into their orbit. The idea is that the Shuttle becomes a fully adequate alternative to unmanned cargo rockets. The launch of the satellites was to become cheaper in this way. However, space shuttle missions have never become more cost-efficient than unmanned rockets.

June 18-24, 1983

Sally Ride is the first American woman to fly into space. She was on board the seventh space shuttle mission.

November 28-December 8, 1983

Spacelab, a European designed and built laboratory is with the ninth space shuttle mission, transported in the payload bay. There is also one European aboard the shuttle, German astronaut Ulf Merbold. Together with his American colleagues, he

TO ORBITER

carried out a number of experiments. Spacelab flew again under American and Japanese flags.

April 6-13, 1984

The first time a malfunctioning satellite is repaired in space. The Solar Maximum Mission satellite failed to function nine months after its launch and was secured and repaired by the shuttle crew. This became an important task to be executed by space shuttles but over time it became apparent that it was possible in a few cases only.

April 12-19, 1985

Republican Senator Jake Garn enters space as the first American politician. Space shuttle missions were pronounced safe enough for people with only minimum training. Garn was

The first three European astronauts were selected in 1978. They were (from left to right): Dutchman Wubbo Ockels, Swiss Claude Nicollier and German Ulf Merbold. Merbold was the first to go into space, in 1983, and made two more missions afterwards – one of them was a month onboard Mir as the first West-European. Ockels made a mission in 1985 and Nicollier completed four space flights. The trio poses in front of a model of Spacelab, in the European designed laboratory built to fit into space shuttle's payload bay.

sick to death during most of the flight and served as a guinea pig for medical experiments. A representative of the Democrats flew into orbit one and a half years later.

January 28, 1986

73 seconds after the liftoff, Space Shuttle Challenger explodes. All seven crew members are killed, among them a teacher, Christa McAuliffe. The Space Shuttle program came to an immediate halt. A commission claimed that under the circumstances, Challenger should never have been launched. NASA launched the Orbiter under immense pressure from all involved.

February 20, 1986

The first part of the new Russian orbital station, Mir (meaning 'peace' and 'world') is launched. Mir was a successor of Salyut and was considerably larger: in the years to come various modules were attached with living and working space for the cosmonauts. In 2001, Mir was deactivated and navigated to crash into the ocean.

September 29-October 3, 1988

Space shuttle flights resume some 32 months after the crash of the Challenger. The flight was carried out in a space shuttle that was upgraded with dozens of improvements. The mission was carried out under enhanced safety measures.

November 15, 1988

The Russians launch their own space shuttle, called Buran ('snowstorm'). The spacecraft, very similar to the American Space Shuttle, is unmanned and lands automatically after it finishes two full orbits of Earth. Later, there were more test flights, but lack of financial means was behind the fact that it has never flown with a crew onboard. The project was eventually halted. On the launch base in Baikonur, the towering structures built for Buran's liftoffs are still visible. In Gorky Park in Moscow, you can see a test model of Buran that has been transformed into a children's attraction.

April 24-29, 1990

The Hubble Telescope is unloaded from the payload bay of Space Shuttle Discovery. It is an enormous piece of equipment which was to be visited during future missions. The Hubble was designed so that it could be easily approached and maintained by space shuttle astronauts and kept it in operation as long as possible.

January 8, 1994

Russian doctor Valeri Polyakov flies to Mir. He eventually stayed there for 437 days, a record unbeaten till this day. Apparently, the record will be broken only when people start traveling in the direction of the Moon and Mars. Astronauts are not intended to stay onboard the ISS for longer than several months.

February 3-11, 1994

The first time a Russian cosmonaut, Sergey Krikalev, flies into space in a space shuttle. The cooperation between the former enemies was generally welcomed by both sides. The Americans wanted experience with long-term missions in an orbital station and the Russians badly needed the money for Mir's maintenance.

Christa McAuliffe receives instructions for wearing her helmet during training.

October 3, 1994

The first astronaut of the European Space Agency (ESA) is given a chance to fly to Mir. German Ulf Merbold spends nearly a month at the orbital station. It was Merbold who became the first European on board the space shuttle in 1983.

March 14, 1995

American Norman Thagard departs for Mir. He stayed there for 115 days. Thagard traveled in a Soyuz capsule with two Russians. In the coming years, there were ten more dockings of space shuttle and Mir. Thagard closely observed the way training in Russia was conducted as well as manners on board. He claimed that he felt lonely due to limited Russian speaking ability. Thagard learnt Russian especially for this flight but nevertheless it did not help him to fit in. He considered the experience on board rather unfriendly.

March 22, 1996

Space Shuttle Atlantis transports Shannon Lucid to Mir. She was the first woman to stay at the station for a longer period of time (six months approximately). The next two years in

Norman Thagard

space were characterized by a permanent presence of Americans.

This is Shannon Lucid on board Mir.

February 23, 1997

A fire broke out on Mir. It was caused by oxygen generator failure. The cosmonauts had to put gas masks on and within fifteen minutes the fire was brought under control. The interior of the station was blackened by the smoke.

An unmanned Progress cargo ship collides with Mir during an approach maneuver. The accident results in heavy damage, one of the modules is unusable. Fortunately, there are no victims, but it is a small wonder. For Mir, 1997 turned out to be truly catastrophic: various pieces of equipment failed and on top of it, there was a fire. In the USA, it was widely debated if it was still safe to send Americans to the aging space station.

October 29 – November 7, 1998

More than 36 years after his history shaping space flight, John Glenn, 77, once again flies in the direction of space. He became by far the oldest astronaut in history. He served as a medical guinea pig and at the same time as a NASA public relations focal point.

November 20, 1998

Zarya (meaning 'dawn'), the first part of the International Space Station (ISS) is launched by a Russian rocket. In the years to come, nearly all American and Russian space missions will serve the purpose of assembling this station. Europe, Canada and Japan joined their efforts on the project. The ISS is the most ambitious and most expensive technological project in history.

Approach maneuver of Progress cargo ship in the dark, photographed from the ISS. In the background is Earth's horizon, dimly lit by the rising sun.

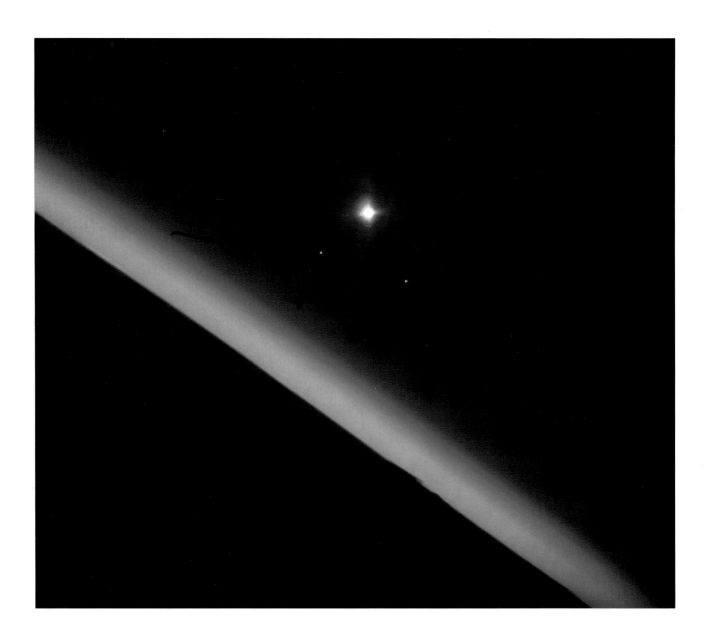

Like a tank commander, the 77 year old John Glenn sits in an armored vehicle in which he exercises launch pad evacuation together with his crew members. The first American to orbit the Earth in 1962 and former senator, got another opportunity to fly into space in 1998. Despite his age, his organism was healthy and fit enough to be able to carry out the mission.

October 31, 2000

The first team of astronauts departs to the ISS orbital station to take up their quarters. The crew consists of Russians Sergey Krikalev, Yuri Gidzenko and American commander William Shepherd.

March 23, 2001

After fifteen years of loyal service, the Mir orbital station reached the end of its existence. The 140 ton object was brought down to the Pacific Ocean. In total, the station accommodated 104 people, 42 of them Russian cosmonauts. The rest were predominantly Americans who spent mostly shorter periods of time onboard the station.

Shepherd, Gidzenko and Krikalev a few hours before their liftoff

April 28, 2001

American billionaire Dennis Tito, the first space tourist, was only able to spend eight days on board the ISS.

February 1, 2003

In re-entry, the Space Shuttle Columbia explodes. The seven crew members had no hope of surviving. The space shuttle

Mir, as photographed in June 1998 from approaching the Space Shuttle Discovery. This was to be the ninth docking of the American spacecraft at the Russian space station.

program was temporarily held off until the middle of 2005. With the Soyuz capsule, the Russians took over the duty of supplying the ISS. But the accident meant an end to the further extension of the station. Bigger parts can be transported only by means of spacecrafts.

The crew of the Soyuz TM34 flight gives a press conference in 2001. The following year Italian Roberto Vittori (left), Russian Yuri Gidzenko and South African Mark Shuttleworth flew to the ISS orbital space station. Shuttleworth was the second astronaut to pay the bill for his journey (some 20 million American dollars) out of his own pocket.

Surrounded by Russian military, American multimillionaire Dennis Tito visits the fortieth space flight anniversary celebration of Yuri Gagarin's mission in Moscow, 2001. Tito was the first astronaut to use his own financial resources for a space journey. He was happy to pay twenty million American dollars for his flight.

October 15, 2003

Yang Li Wei, a 38 year old pilot, becomes the first Chinese in space. He was launched in Shenzhou (meaning 'divinity'), a capsule designed in his own country. China thus became the third country (after Russia and the United States) to send humans to space. The Chinese promise an ambitious space program based on manned missions.

Yang Li Wei is greeted by his countrymen after his return to Earth.

14 january 2004

President Bush announces that he would like to set a new course for the American space program; he wants Americans back on the Moon's surface and says that reaching Mars should become the present goal of American space exploration.

The Moon and Mars (the small red point to the right) as seen from the International Space Station.

List of Terms

Apollo: American Moon mission project which reached its climax with six manned landings on the Moon between 1969 and 1972.

Baikonur: Launch base in Kazakhstan which saw liftoffs of nearly all manned Russian rockets.

ESA: European Space Agency, an organization of fifteen European countries which cooperate on space flights.

Gemini: Two-seater capsule launched in the sixties by Americans as a run-up to the Apollo Moon project. Gemini capsules carried out successful space maneuvers and were used for the first American spacewalks.

ISS: International Space Station, orbital station, the assembly of which started in 1998. It is the focal point for current space flights. These days, the station accommodates two crew members and consists of a number of modules and compartments that have been attached in recent years to extend the work and living area. The United States, Russia, Europe, Japan and Canada participate financially on this project.

Johnson Space Center: The most important training center used by American astronauts is based in Houston. It also houses the flight control center which maintains communication with spacecrafts that orbit the Earth.

Kennedy Space Center: Launch base in Florida used exclusively for sending American manned spacecrafts to space.

Mercury: The first American-manned space capsule. Between 1961 and 1963, it was launched six times with only one astronaut onboard.

Mir: Former Russian space station which orbited the Earth in the period of 1986 and 2001.

NASA: National Aeronautics and Space Administration, the American space agency.

Progress: Unmanned cargo ship used by Russians to supply the ISS (and previously also the Salyut and Mir orbital stations). Looks very much like Soyuz.

Spacewalk: An excursion for astronauts outside their spacecraft. It requires a special spacesuit which must be anchored with a cable to the ship. Spacewalks are necessary for repairs as well as for replacing various pieces of external equipment.

Salyut: Russian space stations, seven in total, which accommodated astronauts in the seventies and eighties. Salyut 7 was replaced by the much bigger Mir in 1986.

Skylab: American space station. Between 1973 and 1974, it housed successively three crews of three astronauts each. Each crew stayed there for several months.

Soyuz:	Capsule used by Russians to travel to space and back to Earth. Unlike a space shuttle, Soyuz can not be reused. There is enough room for only three astronauts. The module is no longer used for independent flights; it merely serves as a sort of a taxi transporting people to space stations. Earlier, they were Salyut and Mir, currently it is the ISS.
Space Shuttle:	Spacecraft of American provenance has been in use ever since 1981. Currently, there are three Orbiters (airplane-like spacecrafts) in operation: Discovery, Atlantis, and Endeavor. Challenger and Columbia were destroyed in accidents. These days, The space shuttle mainly transports people and material to the ISS orbital station.
Star City:	Russian cosmonauts' training center. It is located near Moscow.
Flight control:	Control center which supervises space flights. American mission control is in Houston; Russian 'TSuP' is in Moscow.
Voshkod:	An enlarged Vostok capsule flew into space twice: in 1964 and 1965. One of the two missions had two, the other three people on board.
Vostok:	The first Soviet manned space capsule. Between 1961 and 1963 it was used for three flights (the first with Gagarin, the last with Tereshkova on board).

Illustrations

All the photos taken courtesy of National Aeronautics and Space Administration (NASA) with the following exceptions:

Luc van den Abeelen: 60, 65 above, 315
Associated Press: 14, 48, 200 below, 204 below, 207, 291 above, 295, 316
Chris van den Berg: 38
Frans Blok: 279, 282/283
Canadian Space Agency: 19 above, 28
European Space Agency (Stéphane Corvaja, Anneke van der Geest et. al.): 17, 22, 33, 34, 37, 40, 41, 43, 49, 52, 53 above, 55, 56, 57 below, 59, 64, 70, 79, 89, 93, 103, 114, 123, 127 above, 130, 136, 137, 157, 178, 188 below, 194/195, 196, 197, 198, 199, 200 below, 201, 202, 204 below, 205, 206, 215, 236, 307, 312
RSC Energia: 54, 146, 208, 242, 244 below, 248
Sander Koenen : 5, 47, 59 above, 61, 63
TNO : 42
Mark Traa: 49 below, 62
Bert Vis: 229 below, 231, 232 above

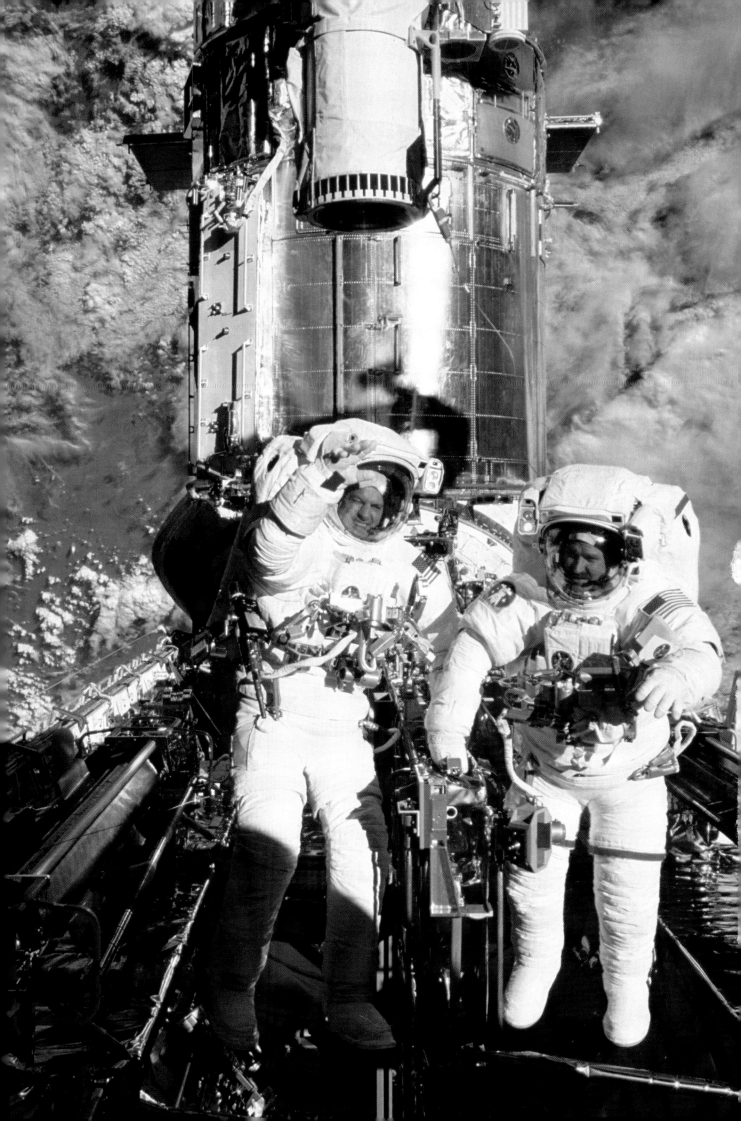